BURT FRANKLIN: BIBLIOGRAPHY & REFERENCE SERIES 290

A

CATALOGUE

OF THE

BOOKS AND PAMPHLETS

ISSUED FROM THE

PRESS OF JOEL MUNSELL

𝕭𝖎𝖇𝖑𝖎𝖔𝖙𝖍𝖊𝖈𝖆 𝕸𝖚𝖓𝖘𝖊𝖑𝖑𝖎𝖆𝖓𝖆

A

CATALOGUE

OF THE

BOOKS AND PAMPHLETS

ISSUED FROM THE

PRESS OF JOEL MUNSELL

FROM THE YEAR

1828 TO 1870

BURT FRANKLIN
NEW YORK

Published by BURT FRANKLIN
235 East 44th St., New York, N.Y. 10017
Originally Published: 1872
Reprinted: 1969
Printed in the U.S.A.

Library of Congress Card Catalog No.: 76-104694
Burt Franklin: Bibliography and Reference Series 290

BIBLIOGRAPHY

OF

MUNSELL IMPRINTS.

------·•·------

1828.

MUNSELL, JOEL. Albany Minerva. 8°, pp. 64.

> This was printed while I was a clerk in a bookstore, and less than twenty years of age. I went along North and South Market streets one day and procured one hundred and fifty subscribers for a semi-monthly paper at 37½ cents a quarter; purchased a small font of types, prepared the copy and set up the types in the store, at leisure moments; worked off the paper at night on a Ramage press, with balls; and the next morning delivered it at the doors of my subscribers. On the morning of the 12th Feb., I announced the death of DeWitt Clinton, at the same hour with the daily papers. I retired from this enterprise at the end of the quarter to take a situation on a daily newspaper as compositor, and did not go into business until

1834.

ALBANY Microscope. Folio.

> Published in connection with Henry D. Stone, at No. 26 Beaver street.

BROWN, PAUL. The Radical and Advocate of Equality; presenting a Series of Expostulatory Animadversions on the present state of Practical Politics and Morals, with a view to an Access of Improvement, addressed to the People of the United States. 12°, pp. 170.

> Paul, unable to struggle successfully with competition, and despising traffic, thought that property should be divided. Of the 500 copies printed, most of them were used for wrapping paper.

1835.

SPECIMEN of Printing Types in the Foundery of Nathan Lyman. 8°.

> Not on file.

1836.

INCORPORATION and By-Laws of the Mutual Insurance Company of the City and County of Albany, passed May 3, 1836. 12°, pp. 12.

PRIEST, JOSIAH. The Robber; or a Narrative of Pye and the Highwayman; being a detailed and particular Account of an Attempted Robbery of the Inn of John Pye, between the Cities of Albany and Troy, N. Y., in 1808, and of the Outlaw's final Capture and End; as related by Mrs. Pye herself, and others who were most intimately acquainted with the whole tragical affair. Together with a History of the Old Man of the Mountain, or the Gold Hunters of Joes Hills. 8vo, pp. 32.

> In October, 1836, I purchased a job printing office of Thomas G. Wait at No. 58 State street, and the first work printed there was

WELLSTEED, JOHN. A Practical Treatise on Sheep. Intended as a Guide to the Selection, Formation and Systematic Management of the Breeding, Wether and Grazing Flocks, with Observations upon the Culture of Turnips, and the Utility and Advantages of the Sheep Fold. 8°, pp. 36.
2,000 copies. Mr. Wellsteed was an English grazier, who had just arrived in this country with his wife, and the latter was thought to be the author of the work.

1837.

BLOODGOOD, S. DEWITT. Coal Lands. 8°.
100 copies. Not on file.

BLOODGOOD, S. DEWITT. Pamphlet. 8°.
250 copies. Not on file.

CATALOGUE OF BOOKS in the Library of the Young Men's Association of the City of Albany, 1837. 12°, pp. 33.

CATALOGUE OF BOOKS in the Sunday School Library of St. Peter's Church, Albany. 16°, pp. 23.
100 copies.

CATALOGUE of the First Presbyterian Church Sunday School Library. 16°, pp. 36.

CATECHISM. 18mo.
2,000 copies. Not on file.

EYSTER, DAVID. Minutes of the Seventh Session of the Hartwick Synod of the Evangelical Lutheran Church in the state of New York; convened at Cobleskill, Schoharie county, Sept., 1837. 8°, pp. 40.
500 copies.

HALE, BENJAMIN. An Inaugural Address, delivered in the Chapel of Geneva College, Dec. 21, 1836. 2d edition, 8°, pp. 32.

HOLMES, EDWIN. Minutes of the Particular Synod of Albany; convened at Schenectady, May, 1837. 8°, pp. 29.
200 copies.

IN THE COURT for the Correction of Errors, Nathan Doane, etc., vs. Zebulon Shepherd, Error Book. 8°, pp. 29.

KENT, JAMES. Opinion of Chancellor Kent on the Usury Laws. 8°, pp. 12.

MINUTES of the Rensselaerville Baptist Association. 8°, pp. 12.
500 copies. Not on file.

PRIEST, JOSIAH. Stories of Early Settlers in the Wilderness: embracing the Life of Mrs. Priest, late of Otsego county, N. Y., with various and interesting accounts of others; the first Raftsmen of the Susquehanna; a Short Account of Brant, the British Indian Chief; and of the Massacre of Wyoming. Embellished with a large and beautiful engraving. By Josiah Priest, author of several Books, Pamphlets, etc. 8°, pp. 40.
15,000 copies.

PRIEST, JOSIAH.   The Anti-Universalist, or History of the Fallen Angels of the Scriptures; Proofs of the Being of Satan and of Evil Spirits, and many other Curious Matters connected therewith.   Embellished with twelve engravings.   By Josiah Priest, author of The Millenium, American Antiquities, etc.   8°, 2 parts in 1 vol.

   5,000 copies. This work was issued under peculiar disadvantages. The paper delivered for it was wretched, and the engravings were worse. But the author could not bear delay, so the work proceeded. The agents got their books just as an extraordinary money panic came on, and could not collect any thing for them; hence their sureties were sued, and full six years elapsed before the business was closed up.

SMITH, CHARLES A.   Minutes of the Forty-second Synod of the Evangelical Lutheran Ministerium of the State of New York, and Adjacent Parts; convened at Churchtown, N. Y., Sept. 9, 1837.   8°, pp. 16.

   500 copies.

SMITH, CHARLES A.   The Catechumen's Guide, prepared with special reference to the Wants of the Evangelical Lutheran Church in the United States.   12°, pp. 312.

   1,000 copies.

SMITH, CHARLES A.   The Lutheran Pulpit, and Monthly Religious Magazine.   8°, 2 vols. in 1.

   1,000 copies.

VAN SCHAICK, JOHN BLEECKER.   The Constitution of the Albany Military Association, and its By-Laws, adopted Jan. 21, 1829.   8°, pp. 62, vignette.

   175 copies.

VERMILYE, THOMAS E.   An Introductory Address to the Course of Lectures before the Young Men's Association for Mutual Improvement in the city of Albany, delivered Dec. 19, 1837.   8°, pp. 37.

   1,000 copies.

WATERS, HENRY.   Poema: a Dialogue between Superstition and Philosopher.   16°, pp. 16.

   Two small editions were printed of which this was the first., The author was a resident of Hudson, whose theological notions were peculiar to himself.

YOUNGHANS, GEORGE.   Pamphlet.   8°.

   100 copies. The author was an eccentric Schoharie farmer, of German descent, who had peculiar notions on theology, somewhat discordant with popular ideas. He paid in specie at a time when paper money was under par. Not on file.

1838.

BLOODGOOD, S. DEWITT.   A Treatise on Roads, their History, Character and Utility; being the Substance of Two Lectures delivered before the Young Men's Association of the City of Albany.   12°, pp. 228.

   500 copies. A considerable portion of the edition was burned.

BY-LAWS of the Albany Axe Company.   16°, pp. 8.

CAMPBELL, J. N.   Papal Rome identified with the Great Apostacy predicted in the Scriptures; the Substance of three Discourses addressed to the First Presbyterian Church in Albany, January, 1838.   2d edition, 16°, pp. 105.

   875 copies.

CATALOGUE of Furniture belonging to the Fort Orange Hotel, to be sold at auction by Davis & Jones, on Monday, April 9, 1838. Sale to commence at 10 o'clock A. M., on the Premises. 12°, pp. 12.

CATALOGUE of the Apprentices Library. 16°.
1,000 copies. Not on file.

CATALOGUE of the Trustees, Teachers and Students of Union Village Academy, March, 1838. 12°, pp. 12.

DEAN, AMOS. A Manual of Law for Business Men ; containing, Alphabetically arranged, the Legal Principles of most frequent application to Ordinary Business Transactions, together with References to the Authorities sustaining them. 12°, pp. 242.
1,500 copies. The author was at this time a practicing attorney.

EYRE, JOHN. The Christian Spectator. 12°.
3,000 copies. Not on file. An eccentric Englishman, whose book consisted of his experiences as a pietist and a traveler. He met with much that was distasteful to him, and which became the burden of his book.

FONDEY, WILLIAM H. An Oration before the Young Men's Association for Mutual Improvement in the city of Albany, delivered July 4, 1838. 8°, pp. 40.
500 copies.

HOLMES, EDWIN. Minutes of the Particular Synod of Albany, convened in the City of Hudson, May 2d, 1838. 8°, pp. 38.
200 copies.

LAPE, THOMAS. A Sermon on the Knowledge and Reunion of Christian Friends in Heaven. 8°, pp. 16.
300 copies.

LOWRIE, JAMES. Pamphlet. 8°.
200 copies. Not on file ; theological.

MCNAUGHTON, JAMES. Annual Address before the New York State Medical Society, Feb. 6, 1838. 8°, pp. 32.

PAPERS AND DOCUMENTS relating to the Mohawk and St. Lawrence Rail Road and Navigation Company. 8°, pp. 25.
300 copies. Map.

PROCEEDINGS of the Whig Convention. 8°.
4,000 copies. Not on file.

REGULATIONS of the Evangelical Lutheran Church of St. Peter, in the Town of Rhinebeck, County of Dutchess, State of New York, adopted May, 1838. 12°, pp. 22.
200 copies.

REPORT of Albany Tract Society. 8°, pp. 32.
500 copies.

SMITH, CHARLES A. Discourse on Missions, delivered before the Evangelical Lutheran Ministerium of the State of New York. 8°, pp. 22.
100 copies.

SPRAGUE, WILLIAM B. A Sermon addressed to the Second Presbyterian Congregation in Albany, March 4, 1838, the Sabbath after Intelligence was received that the Hon. Jonathan Cilley, Member of Congress from Maine, had been shot in a Duel with the Hon. William J. Graves, Member from Kentucky. 8°, pp. 16.
2,900 copies.

TAYLOR, JANE. The Girl's School Book No. 1, designed for Little Girls as a Reading Book, in Primary or Common Schools. 16°, pp. 96.
2,000 copies. Mrs. Taylor was the wife of the publisher, J. Orville Taylor.

TWENTY-SEVENTH Annual Report of the Albany Bible Society. 12°, pp. 12.
400 copies.

VERMILYE, THOMAS E. Zion the City of Solemnities: a Sermon preached at the Dedication of the Third Reformed Protestant Dutch Church in the city of Albany, Dec. 17, 1837. 8°, pp. 29.
600 copies.

WORDS AND ORDER of a Selection of Sacred Music, to be performed by the Choir of the North Dutch Church, with the Assistance of Professors and Amateurs, on Thursday evening, Dec. 25th; the Proceeds of which are to be appropriated to the Contingent Expenses of the Choir. 12°, pp. 4.
A second edition was printed in 8 pages, octavo.

1839.

ANNUAL REPORT, Proceedings and Address, of the New York State Colonization Society. 8°, pp. 8.
2,150 copies.

BECK, T. ROMEYN. Statistics of the Medical Colleges of the United States. 8°, pp. 12.

BEDFORD, GUNNING S. Introductory Lecture before the Albany Medical College, delivered Oct. 1, 1839. 8°, pp. 23.

BRICE, JAMES. Secrets of the Mount Pleasant State Prison Revealed and Exposed. 8°, pp. 277.
This was a vindication of the author, who was imprisoned for perjury, and contained also his prison experience, and other personal topics. 2,000 copies printed.

BY-LAWS of the Journeymen Stone Cutters' Association of the cities of Albany and Troy. 16°, pp. 16.

BY-LAWS of the Medical Society of the State of New York, with the Rules of Order, etc., etc. Prepared for the use of the Society at its Annual Meeting. 8°, pp. 23.

CIRCULAR AND CATALOGUE of the Faculty and Students of the College of Physicians and Surgeons of the Western District of the State of New York, in Fairfield, Herkimer county, 1838–39. 8°, pp. 16.
12,000 copies.

DEAN, AMOS.   Introductory Lecture before the Young Men's Association for Mutual Improvement in the City of Albany, delivered Dec. 17, 1839. 8°, pp. 33.
750 copies.

EYSTER, DAVID.   Minutes of the Ninth Session of the Hartwick Synod of the Evangelical Lutheran Church in the State of New York, convened at Middleburgh, Schoharie county, Sept., 1839.   8°, pp. 32.
500 copies.

HAMMOND, WELLS S.   Oration delivered at Cherry Valley, on the Fourth day of July, 1839.   8°, pp. 16.
600 copies.

HULL, LAURENS.   Annual Address delivered before the Medical Society of the State of New York, Feb. 6, 1839.   8°, pp. 14.

McKEE, ROBERT.   Lectures on Botany, delivered at the Albany Female Academy.   8°, pp. 20.
250 copies. Mr. McKee was a clergyman of the Scotch Presbyterian sect, who died the following year at the age of 42.

McKERCHER, DUNCAN.   Catalogue of D. McKercher's Circulating Library, at No. 32 Green street.   18°, pp. 38.
500 copies.

McLACHLAN, D.   Outlines of Therapeiology, or the Science of Remedies; for the Use of Students attending Albany Medical College.   12°, pp. 16.

MUNSELL, JOEL.   Outlines of the History of Printing, and Sketches of the Early Printers.   8°, pp. 32.
This was taken almost entirely from Thomas's History of Printing, to which my name was unwisely attached as the author or compiler. It was issued merely to circulate as a specimen of printing. Edition 100 copies.

PHRENOLOGICAL Chart, giving a Description of the Phenomena of the Human Mind : designed to assist Man in obtaining a Knowledge of himself.   12°, pp. 12.
500 copies.

PRYNNE, ARTHUR. [Joel Munsell.]   The Full and True History of the Conquest of Mexico by Cortez, one of the most astonishing Military Achievements on Record, in which about 500 Spaniards cut their way through more than 150,000 Indian Warriors, to the Golden City of the Sun.   By Capt. Bernal Diaz del Castillo, one of the Conquerors.   Translated from the Spanish in which it was originally written.   8°, pp. 32.
This was a *chap-book*, condensed from the well known work by Diaz, got up to aid in filling a temporary lull in business.

RAWLS, HENRY & Co.   Catalogue of Philosophical and Astronomical Instruments, illustrative of the Physical Sciences, including Mechanics, Pneumatics, Hydrostatics, Hydraulics, Optics, Astronomy, Electricity, Galvanism, Magnetism, Chemistry, Acoustics.   8°, pp. 16.
500 copies.

REESE, DAVID M.   Introductory Lecture before the Albany Medical College, delivered Oct. 1, 1839.   8°, pp. 22.
500 copies.

REPORT relative to the Finances of St. Peter's Church.   8°, pp. 7.
300 copies.

SELECT CATALOGUE of Cheap and Elegant Music, for the Piano Forte, etc., for sale by William G. Boardman, at his Piano Forte Ware Rooms and Music Saloon, sign of the Golden Lyre, No. 80 State street, Albany 12°, pp.. 36.

SMITH, CHARLES A.   Minutes of the Forty-third Synod of the Evangelical Lutheran Ministerium of the State of New York, and Adjacent Parts, Convened in St. Peter's Church, Rhinebeck, Dutchess County, on the 8th and following days of September, 1838.   8°, pp. 19.

SUPREME COURT.   The President, Directors and Company of the Commercial Bank of Albany, vs. Erastus Corning and James Porter, survivors of Henry Barstow, deceased.   Opinions of Daniel Cady and Hiram Denio, Esqs., two of the Referees in the above Causes in which Gideon Hawley, Esq., the other Referee, also concurred.   8°, pp. 24.

TWENTY-EIGHTH Annual Report of the Albany Bible Society.   12°, pp. 12.
400 copies.

VERMILYE, THOMAS E.   A Funeral Discourse occasioned by the Death of the Hon. Stephen Van Rensselaer, delivered in the North Dutch Church, Albany, on Sabbath Evening, Feb. 3, 1839.   8°, pp. 43.
2,000 copies.

WARREN, GEORGE.   Report of the Directors of the Albany Coal Company.   8°, pp. 10.
The committee consisted of Barent P. Staats, George Warren and John Thomas. It was the result of an experiment of citizens to furnish coal at a cheaper rate than was done by the dealers.

1840.

BLOODGOOD, S. D. W.   Pamphlet.   8°, pp. 16.
500 copies. Not on file.

CATALOGUE of the Library of the Young Men's Association for Mutual Improvement in the city of Albany.   12°, pp. 50.

CATALOGUE of the Sabbath School Library of the Dutch Reformed Church.
150 copies. Not on file.

CLUTE, JOHN BT.   Annual Report of the President of the Young Men's Association for Mutual Improvement in the city of Schenectady, presented May 13, 1840.   8°, pp. 18.
350 copies.

CONSTITUTION of the Albany Phrenological Society; founded March 16, 1840.   18°, pp. 8.

DAVIS.   Address before the New York State Medical Society.   8°.
60 copies. Not on file.

DEAN, AMOS.   Manual of Medical Jurisprudence; for the use of his class.   12°, pp. 58.
800 copies.

GRIMES, J. STANLEY. Outlines of Grimes's New System of Phrenology. 12°, pp. 12, cuts.

> 2,000 copies. Mr. Grimes was a practical shoemaker, who got off the bench to teach phrenology. He was successful in keeping his audiences in good humor by an abundance of comical illustrations; but he soon abandoned it for the law. He taught a different classification from other phrenologists, in some respects.

HOLMES, EDWIN. Minutes of the Particular Synod of Albany ; convened in the City of Albany, May 2, 1840. 8°, pp. 38.

> 200 copies.

HORSFORD, E. N. Report on the Phrenological Classification of J. Stanley Grimes. 12°, pp. 44.

> 1,500 copies. 1,300 copies, 2d edition.

HULL, LAURENS. Annual Address delivered before the Medical Society of the State of New York, Feb., 1840. 8°, pp. 15.

> 60 copies.

IN THE COURT for the Trial of Impeachments and the Correction of Errors. Robertson Whiteside vs. the People, ex. rel. Ebenezer P. Upham. Error Book. 8°, pp. 23.

> 50 copies.

KIP, WILLIAM INGRAHAM. Our National Sins : A Sermon, preached in St. Paul's Church in the City of Albany, on the Evening of the twentieth Sunday after Trinity, MDCCCXL. 8°, pp. 21.

> 750 copies.

KIP, WILLIAM INGRAHAM. The Manifestation of the Truth : a Sermon preached in St. Paul's Church in the City of Albany on Sexagesima Sunday, MDCCCXL, being the first after the Consecration of the Edifice to the Worship of God. 8°, pp. 24.

McNAUGHTON, JAMES. Case of Sudden Death from Rupture of the Spermatic Vein, read before the Medical Society of the State of New York, at its Annual Session in 1840. 8°, pp. 8.

OLCOTT, THOMAS W. Address delivered before the Albany Phrenological Society, at its Meeting in the Female Academy on the Evening of April 2, 1840. 8°, pp. 10.

> A Phrenological Society was organized at the close of Prof. Grimes's lectures, of which Mr. Olcott was elected president, and this address was delivered under the requirements of the constitution.

PRYNNE, ARTHUR. [J. Munsell.] Prynne's Almanac for 1841, adapted to the use of the Merchant, Mechanic and Farmer ; calculated for the Meridian of Albany, but will answer for any part of the State of New York. 12°, pp. 24.

> 1,000 copies.

REPORT of a Committee of the Medical Society of the State of New York on the Subject of Medical Education. 8°, pp. 22.

> 500 copies.

SMITH, S. R. Pocket Manual; containing Selections from the Scriptures in Proof of the Salvation of all Mankind; together with those Passages supposed to favor the Doctrine of Endless Misery ; to which is added, a Brief Explanation of several Scripture Terms. 16°, pp. 59

THOMAS, J. THOMAS.   The Helderberg War.   8°.
1,000 copies.   Not on file.

THE UNIONIST.   Folio.
A daily paper, published in the interest of a faction of the Whigs, for the purpose of advocating the election of Daniel D. Barnard to Congress. It was principally edited by Cicero Loveridge, and the bills were paid by John L. Schoolcraft and James Horner. Hugh J. Hastings began his newspaper career upon this paper in the capacity of clerk.

TILLINGHAST, JOHN L., and JOHN V. N. YATES.   A Treatise on the Principles and Practice, Process, Pleadings and Entries, in cases of Writs of Error; Writs in the nature of Writs of Error ; Appeals and Proceedings in the Nature of Appeals.   8°, pp. iii, 572.
This work was prosecuted so tardily that I was forced to abandon it before it was completed, and it was finished by Hoffman & White.

TRANSACTIONS of the Medical Society of the State of New York.   8°, 4 vols.
These were edited by Dr. T. R. Beck.

TWENTY-NINTH Annual Report of the Albany Bible Society.   12°, pp. 12.

WORTHINGTON, D.   Annual Report of the President of the Young Men's Association for Mutual Improvement in the City of Albany, presented at its Seventh Annual Meeting, Feb. 3, 1840.   8°, pp. 18.
500 copies.

WYCKOFF, ISAAC N.   Stability an Indispensable Element of Usefulness and Greatness.   An address delivered before the Alumni of Rutgers College, July 14, 1840, and inscribed to them by their Consociate.   8°, pp. 27.
500 copies.

YOUNG MEN'S ASSOCIATION.   July 4, 1840, Order of Exercises.   12°, pp. 4.

1841.

ALLEN, E. D.   An Introductory Address to the Course of Lectures before the Young Men's Association for Mutual Improvement in the City of Albany; delivered Nov. 30, 1841.   8°, pp. 34.

BECK, JOHN B.   Observations on Ergot, read before the Medical Society of the State of New York, Feb. 3, 1841.   8°, pp. 16.

BLEECKER, WILLIAM E.   Annual Report of the President of the Young Men's Association for Mutual Improvement in the City of Albany ; presented at its Eighth Annual Meeting, Feb. 1, 1841.   8°, pp. 15.
800 copies.

BY-LAWS of Independence Hook and Ladder Company, No. 1, of the City of Albany.   18°, pp. 8.

CAMPBELL, J. N.   A Discourse on the occasion of the Death of James King, Esq., delivered in the First Presbyterian Church of Albany, on the Evening of the Communion Sabbath, June 27, 1841.   8°, pp. 21.
300 copies.

CATALOGUE of the Corporation, Faculty and Students of Troy Conference Academy, West Poultney, Vt., for the Academic Year, 1841.   8°, pp. 20.

DAVIS, WILLIAM P.   The Pastor's Farewell: containing a Series of Discourses, delivered in view of a dissolution of the Pastoral Relation. 12°, pp. 225.
2,000 copies.

DEAN, AMOS.   Address delivered before the Young Men's State Association of the State of New York, at their first Annual Meeting, at Geneva, Sept. 2, 1841.   8°, pp. 31.   Appendix, pp. 3.
1,200 copies.

ELY, SUMNER.   Annual Address delivered before the Medical Society of the State of New York, Feb. 3, 1841.   8°, pp. 16.

HOLMES, EDWIN.   Minutes of the Particular Synod of Albany ; convened in the city of Schenectady, May 5, 1841.   8°, pp. 41.
200 copies.

KNOX, JOHN P.   A Brief History of the Protestant Reformed Dutch Church in Nassau, preached Jan. 10, 1841.   8°, pp. 31.
300 copies.

NEWLAND, LUKE F.   Programme and Descriptive Sketch of Neukomn's Oratorio of David, to be performed by the Professors and Amateurs of Albany, April, 1841.   12°, pp. 12.
500 copies. Another edition of 700 copies was printed. Mr. Newland was a Scotchman, a gentleman of good presence, by profession a working jeweler, who took great interest in music, and was foremost in all enterprises of this kind for a good many years.

NEW YORK STATE MECHANIC, under the Direction of the New York State Mechanic Association.   4°, 2 vols.
3,000 copies.

PRIEST, JOSIAH.   History of the Early Adventures of Washington among the Indians of the West.   8°, pp. 32.
4,000 copies. Mr. Priest involved Washington in a love affair with an Irish girl whom he met in the wilderness. A copy of the work was called for some years after it was printed. by a person, who remarked with much emphasis, that he had never found any mention of this episode in the life of Washington in any other account of him. Priest was undoubtedly the greatest inventor of ancient history and biography of his time.

PRIEST, JOSIAH.   The Fort Stanwix Captive, or New England Volunteer, being the extraordinary Life and Adventures of Isaac Hubbell among the Indians of Canada and the West, in the War of the Revolution, and the Story of his Marriage with the Indian Princess, now first published from the lips of the Hero himself.   8°, pp. 64.
6,000 copies.

SCOTT, DAVID.   Distinctive Principles of the Reformed Presbyterian Church.   12°, pp. 324.
1,250 copies.

SEARS, REUBEN.   A Discourse delivered in the Presbyterian Church, New Scotland, May 14, 1841 ; the Day of Public Fasting and Prayer, on Account of the Death of William Henry Harrison, late President of the United States.   8°, pp. 23.

SERMON.   8°, pp. 26.
   300 copies. Not on file.

SKINNER, E. W. Webster's Calendar, or the Albany Almanac, for the year of our Lord, 1842.   12°, pp. 36.
   5,000 copies.

SMITH, JAMES. Man, with his Ability through the Atonement to render himself Acceptable to God; with Advice as to the Means of accomplishing it.   8°, pp. 20.
   500 copies.

SQUIER, E. G. Ladies' Magazine.   8°.
   5,000 copies. Not on file. Only a few numbers printed.

THIRTIETH Annual Report of the Albany Bible Society.   12°, pp. 12.
   400 copies. Was prepared for the press by the Rev. J. N. Campbell.

THOMSON, SAMUEL. [John Thomson.] The Thomsonian Materia Medica, or Botanic Family Physician : comprising a Philosophical Theory, the Natural Organization and assumed Principles of Animal and Vegetable Life : to which are added the Description of Plants and their various Compounds : together with Practical Illustrations, including much other useful matter, with Plates.   Thirteenth edition, enlarged, corrected, revised and improved.   8°, pp. 834.
   4,000 copies (?) John Thomson was the son of Samuel Thomson, the founder of the system of medical practice which bears his name. Very little of the matter prepared for the volume was used, because the author met with an English work on anatomy, while the book was in press, which he resolved to adopt, notwithstanding the Thomsonians scouted anatomy up to this time. The botanic plates have been pronounced good. The book was sold at $20, which included a right to practice. Any one buying a book became a practitioner. The old gentleman was not wholly pleased with the work of his son, but the latter called together a number of the faculty at his house, and induced them to formally adopt and commend the work, and the father was thereby silenced.

1842.

ANGUS, ROBERT. Charges and Specifications preferred by Brigadier-General John Groesbeck, commandant of the 61st Brigade of Infantry of the Militia of the state of New York, against —— a ——— of a company in the 246th Regiment of Infantry of the Militia of the State of New York.   12°, pp. 14.

BECK, JOHN B. An Historical Sketch of the State of American Medicine before the Revolution ; being the Annual Address delivered before the Medical Society of the State of New York.   Feb. 1, 1842.   8°, pp. 35.
   100 copies.

BECK, JOHN B. Observations on some of the Signs of Live and Still Birth, in their applications to Medical Jurisprudence.   8°, pp. 8.

BY-LAWS of Iris Lodge, No. 359, I. O. of O. F., Coeymans, N. Y.   12°, pp. 8.

CATALOGUS Sodalium Societatis K. A. Novi Eboraci, in Collegio Concordiæ, MD.CCCXLII.   8°, pp. 23.

HOLMES, EDWIN.   Minutes of the Particular Synod of Albany ; convened
in the Village of West Troy, May 4, 1842.   8°, pp. 29.
200 copies.

SKINNER, ELISHA W.   Webster's Calendar, or the Albany Almanac, for
the year of our Lord, 1843.   12°, pp. 36.
4,000 copies.   This was the last edition published by any of the old firm of Web-
sters & Skinners, by whom it had been continued sixty years.

SMYTH, CHARLES T.   Annual Report of the President of the Young Men's
Association for Mutual Improvement in the City of Albany, presented
at its Ninth Annual Meeting, Feb. 7, 1842.   8°, pp. 14.

SQUIER, E. G.   American Poetry.   12°, pp. 92.
1,200 copies.   Work never completed — never sold — was never paid for.

STEWART, JOHN G. and MORTON, CHARLES S.   The Northern Star and
Freemen's Advocate.   Folio.
Weekly paper published in the interest of the Africo-American race.   Was of short
continuance.

TAYLOR, THOMAS.   Precedents of Wills, drawn conformably to the Revised Statutes of the State of New York ; with Practical Notes, comprising the duty of Executors, Administrators and Guardians.   Dedi-
cated, by permission, to the Hon. James Vanderpoel.   2 vols., 8°.
750 copies.

THIRTY-FIRST Annual Report of the Albany Bible Society.   12°, pp. 12.
400 copies.   Prepared by the Rev. J. N. Campbell.

TILLINGHAST, JOHN L.   Return of the Commissioners under the Act to
Improve the Navigation of the Albany Basin, and to extend the opening in the Albany Pier, made to the Mayor, Aldermen and Common-
alty of the City of Albany, Oct., 1842.   8°, pp. 91.
500 copies.

TRANSACTIONS of the State Medical Society for 1842.   8°.
300 copies.   Edited by Dr. T. R. Beck.

1842. 3

APOLOGY for the Holy Dead, by a Student for the Episcopacy.   8°.
100 copies.   Not on file.   One of the pamphlets that grew out of the strictures of the
Rev. John N. Campbell upon the Episcopacy and the Fathers.

BATEY, JOHN.   Thoughts on the Immortality and Future Condition of
Man ; designed for all who deny a Future State, but more especially
as a Reply to Rev. Geo. Storrs's Inquiry, " Are the Souls of the Wicked
Immortal ? "   8°, pp. 55.
500 copies.

BERNARD, DAVID.   A Sermon on the Meaning and Design of Baptism ;
delivered before the First Baptist Church in Albany, on the first Lord's
Day in April, 1843.   8°, pp. 24.
1,000 copies.

BIBLE Expositor.
5,000 copies.   Not on file.

BLATCHFORD, THOMAS W. Homœopathy Illustrated. An Address, first
delivered before the Rensselaer County Medical Society, at the Annual
Meeting in the City of Troy, June 14, 1852, and by request repeated
before a Popular Audience, June 18, 1842. 8°, pp. 83.
150 copies.

BUSH, WALTER R. Tenth Annual Report of the President of the Young
Men's Association for Mutual Improvement in the City of Albany,
presented at its Ninth Annual Meeting, Feb. 6, 1843. 8°, pp. 16.

CAMPBELL, JOHN N. Catalogue of Communicants belonging to the First
Presbyterian Church, Albany, from its foundation to the year 1843.
12°, pp. 23.
500 copies.

CATALOGUE and Circular of the Albany Medical College. 8°, pp. 20.
2,000 copies.

CHURCH Library of the First Presbyterian Church of the City of Albany.
16°, pp. 8.

CIRCULAR of the New York State Mechanics' Association. 8°, pp. 24.
500 copies.

CURTIS, NEWTON M. The Bride of the Northern Wilds. A tale. 8°, pp. 64.
3,000 copies. The author of this pamphlet was a resident of Charlton, Saratoga
county, of limited education, a whiskey drinking, tobacco chewing, profane swear-
ing, and squalid specimen of humanity. A benevolent individual aided him in the
publication of his books in the hope of reclaiming him ; but he soon relapsed, and
swindled his benefactor. His fictions, however, had a good run.

DOCUMENTS in relation to State Prison Competition. 8°, pp. 12.

EXERCISES had at the Celebration of the Sixth Anniversary of the Fire-
man's Lodge, No. XIX, I. O. O. F., in the Lecture Room of the Young
Men's Association, in the City of Albany, on Tuesday Evening, March
21, 1843. 8°, pp. 27.
Consists of a Poem by A. B. Street, and an Oration by G. W. Clinton.

GESSNER, SOLOMON. The Death of Abel. 18°.
500 copies. Not on file.

HOLMES, EDWIN. Minutes of the Particular Synod of Albany, convened
at the City of Albany, May 3, 1843. 8°, pp. 34.
200 copies.

HUNT, T. B. The Bible Baptist. With additional Notes. 12°, pp. 36.
1,000 copies. Published in the interest of the Presbyterians and others.

I. O. O. F. Addresses. 8°.
500 copies. Not on file.

KIP, WM. I. The History, Object and Proper Observance of the Holy
Season of Lent. 16°, pp. 228.
3,000 copies.

McILVAINE, CHARLES P. The Argument for the Apostolical Succession.
12°, pp. 16.
500 copies.

MUNSELL, JOEL. The Every Day Book of History and Chronology; embracing the Anniversaries of Memorable Persons and Events, in every Period and State of the World, from the Creation to the Present Time; compiled from the most Authentic Sources. 12°, 2 vols.
500 copies.

MUNSELL, JOEL. Webster's Calendar, or the Albany Almanac, for the year of our Lord 1844: Being the latter part of the 68th and beginning of the 69th year of the independence of the United States: The 6557th year of the Julian Period: The latter part of the 5604th and beginning of the 5605th year since the creation of the world, according to the Jews: The 2597th year since the foundation of Rome: The 2620th year of the Olympiads of Greece: The latter part of the 1259th, and beginning of the 1260th year since the *hegira*, or flight of Mahomet. Astronomical Calculations by G. R. Perkins, for the Meridian of Albany, the Capital of the State of New York. 12°, pp. 36.
The publishers of this Almanac, which had gradually decreased in its circulation during several years, now concluded to abandon its publication. I made them the proposition to continue it as long as I should live, although its sale might entirely cease, so that I should need but a single copy for myself; and to pay them a royalty for the title of a certain number of copies each year during their lives. It had now been printed sixty years. I found immediate sale for about twenty thousand.

P. E. S. Tracts for the People, No. 6. Sketches of Sectarianism, No. 3. The Heresy of the Baptists exhibited in Contrast with Holy Scripture, and with the Doctrine and Practice of the Church of God from the Earliest Times. 16°, pp. 36.
1,500 copies. Printed in the interest of Episcopalians.

POTTER, HORATIO. The Christian Instructed in a Holy Life, in a Dialogue between a Minister and his Parishioners. 12°, pp. 16.

POTTER, HORATIO. The Stability of the Church, as seen in her History and her Principles; a Sermon preached in St. Peter's Church, Albany, on Sunday, the 23d day of July, being the sixth Sunday after Trinity. 8°, pp. 24.
1,500 copies.

REPORTS of the Committee on the Sing-Sing and Auburn State Prisons. 8°, pp. 15.
1,000 copies.

RUSSELL, HENRY. Programme of a Vocal Entertainment at the United States Hotel, on Friday Evening, July 21, 1843. 12°, pp. 4.
2,000 copies. He was the most noted vocalist of the day.

SCUDDER, M. L. The Wesleyan Psalmist, or Songs of Canaan, a Collection of Hymns and Tunes designed to be used at Camp Meetings, and at Class and Prayer Meetings, and other Occasions of Social Devotion. 18°, pp. 108.

SERMON on Baptism. 8°.
500 copies. Not on file.

SMITH, S. R.   Universalism the Doctrine of the Primitive Christian Church; a Discourse delivered in the Universalist Church, Albany, N. Y., on the Evening of the Fifth Sunday in January, 1843. 12°, pp. 20.
500 copies.

SPRAGUE, WILLIAM B.   A Sermon addressed to the Fourth Presbyterian Congregation in Albany, on Sabbath Evening, Jan. 1, 1843, in consequence of the Death of their Pastor, Rev. Edward D. Allen; with the Addresses delivered at the Funeral. 8°, pp. 62.
2,000 copies.

SQUIER, E. G.   The Chinese as they are; their moral and social Character, Manners, Customs, Language; with remarks on their Arts and Sciences, Medical Skill, the extent of Missionary Enterprise, etc., by G. Tradescent Lay, Esq.; containing also illustrative and corroborative Notes, additional chapters on the ancient and modern history, ancient and modern intercourse, population, government, civilization, education, literature, etc., of the Chinese, compiled from authentic sources. 8°, pp. 112.
4,000 copies.

STATUTES of the Albany Academy.   Revised and passed Oct. 9, 1829; reprinted with amendments and alterations, Sept., 1843. 12°, pp. 36.

TAYLOR, ISAAC.   Scenes in Asia, for the Amusement and Instruction of Little Tarry-at-Home Travelers. 18°, pp. 123.
500 copies.

THIRTY-SECOND Annual Report of the Albany Bible Society. 12°, pp. 11.

VAN SCHAICK, EGBERT.   Albany Universalist Society Directory. 32°, pp. 31

1844.

ACT OF INCORPORATION and Constitution of the Valatie Fire Engine. Company, No. 4. 18°, pp. 8.

AN APOLOGY for the Holy Dead. 8°, pp. 8.
This was one of the pamphlets written in answer to a series of Sunday Evening Sermons, delivered in the First Presbyterian Church, by the Rev. Dr. J. N. Campbell, which were severely critical of the doctrines of the Fathers, and the apostolical succession claimed by the Episcopalians.

BLATCHFORD, THOMAS W.   Observations on Equivocal Generation; prepared as evidence in a suit for slander. 8°, pp. 14.

BURR, C. C.   Substance of an Extemporaneous Oration, on Irish Repeal, delivered in Troy, Oct. 23, 1844. 8°, pp. 28.
1,000 copies.

CAMPBELL, JOHN N.   The Reformation.   Folio, pp. 36.
1,500 copies.   The sermons of Dr. John N. Campbell against the Episcopacy, cut up into short articles, and published as a periodical.

CAMPBELL, WILLIAM H.   A Funeral Discourse, occasioned by the Death of Rev. Andrew Yates, D. D., delivered before the Classis of Schenectady, in the R. P. Dutch Church, Schenectady, on Sabbath, Nov. 17, 1844. 8°, pp. 34.
600 copies.

CASTLETON MEDICAL COLLEGE. Announcement of the Autumnal Course of Lectures for 1844, and Catalogue of the Students in Attendance on the Spring Session of 1844. 8°, pp. 18.
3,000 copies.

CATALOGUE of Hotel Furniture to be sold by F. M. Stone, on Thursday, Oct. 10th, at 10 o'clock, A. M., on the premises, Rail Road House, Nos. 264 and 266, South Market street, Albany. J. I. Jones, auctioneer. 8°, pp. 7.

CATALOGUE of the Middle Dutch Church Library. ,18°, pp. 24.
75 copies.

CATALOGUE Sale of Substantial and useful City Made Furniture, Bedding, Crockery, etc., being the whole of the articles contained in the Delavan House, No. 77 Broadway, to be sold by Francis M. Stone, Monday morning, April 22, 1844, at 10 o'clock, on the premises. 12°, pp. 42.
300 copies.

CATALOGUS Societatis Fratrum, O. K. E. in Collegio Concordiæ Schenectadiæ; in Rep. Novi Eboraci. 12°, pp. 12.

COLLIER, JASON. Concert to be given by the Choir of the Fourth Presbyterian Church, Broadway, on Monday evening, Dec. 23, 1844, under the direction of J. Collier, commencing at 7¼ o'clock. 8°, pp. 4.
600 copies.

COLUMBUS and his Times. 18°, pp. 196.
1,000 copies.

CONSTITUTION and By-Laws of Hope Lodge, No. 3, of the I. O. of O. F., of the State of New York, instituted 26th of April, 1826. 18°, pp. 32.
200 copies.

CONSTITUTION and By-Laws of Spartan Lodge, No. LXII of I. O. O. F. 12°, pp. 18.

CONSTITUTION, By-Laws, and Rules of Order of Samaritan Lodge, No. 93, I. O. O. F., of the State of New York; located at Albany, Organized August 11, MD.CCCXLIII. 2d edition, 8°, pp. 24.
250 copies.

CONSTITUTION, By-Laws, and Rules of Order of the R. W. M. G. M., Protection of the State of New York. Organized July 13, 1844. 8°, pp. 22.
500 copies.

CURTIS, NEWTON M. Doom of the Tory's Guard. 8°, pp. 96.
6,000 copies. Not on file. The second of a series of Revolutionary novels.

DIXON, JOHN. The Twin Brothers; being the Lives of John and James Dixon, born at Naworth Park, Cumberland, England. 12°, pp. 72.
3,000 copies. Portraits and plates.

DOCUMENTS relating to State Prison. 8°.
1,000 copies. Not on file.

DOUGLASS, D. B. Further Statement of the Facts and Circumstances connected with the Removal of the author from the Presidency of Kenyon College, in answer to the Reply of Trustees, etc. 12°, pp. 71

FISHER, SAMUEL W.   Our Country, its Position, Obligation, and Power; a Sermon delivered in the Fourth Presbyterian Church, Albany, as a Plea for Home Missions, June 23, 1844. 8°, pp. 29.
500 copies.

HOLMES, EDWIN.   Minutes of the Particular Synod of Albany, convened in the City of Albany, May 1, 1844. 8°, pp. 33.
200 copies.

INCORPORATION and By-Laws of the Mutual Insurance Company of the City and County of Albany, passed May 3, 1836. 12°, pp. 12.
1,000 copies.

LAICUS.   The Testimony of the Fathers. 8°, pp. 16.
This was also called out by the controversial sermons of the Rev. Dr. J. N. Campbell, of the First Presbyterian Church.

LAWYER, JOHN D.   Sermon on Baptism, 8°, pp. 68.
600 copies. Not on file.

NEILSON, CHARLES.   An Original, Compiled and Corrected Account of Burgoyne's Campaign, and the Memorable Battle of Bemis's Heights, Sept. 9, and Oct. 7, 1777, from the most authentic sources of information; including many interesting Incidents connected with the same; and a map of the Battle Ground. 12°, pp. 291.
2,000 copies. The author occupied the heights, with his farm, where many visitors naturally resorted during the summer months. His book was intended to answer inquiries, and to aid in selling his property advantageously. But he borrowed money to pay expenses and being already embarrassed, and the sales not so large as was expected, the enterprise hastened his bankruptcy. He claimed that the battle was fought near his house, which was not so.

POTTER, HORATIO.   Rightly dividing the Word of Truth; a Sermon on the Religious Tendencies of the Age, and the consequent Duty of the Christian Minister. Preached in St. Peter's Church, Albany, on Sunday, Nov. 23, 1844. 8°, pp. 33.

PRIEST, JOSIAH.   A copy of the Grants to the Van Rensselaer and Livingston Families, together with a History of the Settlement of Albany, gathered from authentic sources, and published for the information of the Renters. 8°, pp. 32.
2,000 copies.

RELIGIOUS SPECTATOR.   Folio.
1,500 copies, No. 1; 1,000 copies, No. 2. A weekly religious paper, principally edited by the Rev. Dr. William B. Sprague.

REPORT and Speeches on the State Prison Bill in the House of Assembly of the State of New York, 7 March, 1844. 8°, pp. 41.
1,000 copies.

SECOND CONCERT of the Hutchinsons, at the Female Academy, Friday evening, Nov. 8, 1844. 12°, pp. 4.

SMITH and EDWARDS.   National Oration by J. Hyatt Smith, Esq., and Temperance Oration by Isaac Edwards, Esq., delivered at Guilderland Centre, July 4, 1844. Published in order of delivery. 8°, pp. 40.
200 copies.

SPRAGUE, WILLIAM B.   A Sermon on the Danger of Political Strife, addressed to the Second Presbyterian Congregation, Albany, Oct. 3,
1844. 8°, pp. 23.

STREET, ALFRED B.   Drawings and Tintings. 8°, pp. 48.
2,000 copies. This work *fell dead from the press*, so to speak. There was no sale
for it whatever, although it was a season when there was a brisk sale for works got
up in this style.

THE FORTY-SIXTH Anniversary of the Rensselaerville Baptist Association,
held in the Baptist Meeting House of Preston Hollow, Sept. 18, 1844.
12°, pp. 12.
900 copies.

THE SONG OF THE SEXTON, addressed to his Shovel, after the Dedication
of the Albany Cemetery; by Old Mortality. 12°, pp. 8.

THIRTY-THIRD Annual Report of the Albany Bible Society. 12°, pp. 11.
1,000 copies.

WHITE, SAMUEL W.   Address on Insanity before the New York State
Medical Society. 8°, pp. 20.

WOODRUFF, S. M.   Survey of Livingston Manor.
23 copies. No copy on file.

WYCKOFF, ISAAC N.   Christian Example: a Sermon, occasioned by the
Death of Christian Miller, for Sixty Years a Member of the Church, in
the Dutch Reformed connection, delivered in the Second R. P. Dutch
Church, Albany, on Sunday, Dec. 15, 1844. 8°, pp. 31.
500 copies.

1845.

A COMPENDIOUS View of the Doctrinal Sentiments, Discipline, Covenant,
Regular Meetings, and By-Laws of the First Baptist Church. 12°, pp. 15.
1,000 copies.

ALLEN, OTIS. The Duties and Liabilities of Sheriffs, in their various Relations to the Public and to Individuals, as governed by the Principles
of Law, and regulated by the Statutes of New York. 8°, pp. 487.
1,500 copies.

A WORD IN SEASON, to all Churchmen in the Diocese of New York, who
love the Church and deprecate Schism. 8°, pp. 8.

BATES, MERRIT.   How shall a Young Man Cleanse his Way? A Sermon
on the Death of Thomas Patterson, delivered in the Wesleyan Methodist Chapel, Albany, Sept. 21, 1845. 12°, pp. 12.

BECK, T. R., and A. BRIGHAM.   Analysis of the Testimony on the Trial
of Alvin Cornell for Murder, and of the Subsequent Proof, which led
to the Commutation of his Punishment. 8°, pp. 22.

BURR, C. C., and JOHN TANNER.   The Gavel: a Monthly Periodical, devoted to Odd-Fellowship and General Literature. Vol. I, 8°, pp. 324.
2,000 copies. Portraits.

CATALOGUE of 170 splendid European Modern Paintings now exhibiting in Kidd's New Building, No. 68½, Broadway.   Lewis Clark, auctioneer. 8°, pp. 8.

CATALOGUE of the Valuable Private Library of the late Rev. Frederick G. Mayer, containing about four thousand volumes of rare Theological, Medical, Scientific, and Miscellaneous Works, to be sold at auction by F. M. Stone, commencing Thursday evening, Feb. 13, 1845, at half-past six o'clock, and continuing every evening until all is sold.   Joshua I. Jones, auctioneer.   8°, pp. 24.
   500 copies.

CIRCUIT COURT of the United States, May Term, 1845.   William W. Woodworth, administrator and others, vs. Joel Stone.   8°, pp. 8.

CIRCULAR and Catalogue of Mrs. Brinckerhoff's Boarding and Day School for Young Ladies, Albany.   12°, pp. 8.

CIRCULAR and Catalogue of the Albany Female Academy.   8°, pp.
   There seems to have been a second one printed this year in Aug.   1,500 copies.   500 copies.   Not on file under this year.

CONSTITUTION and By-Laws of Engine Company, No. 12.   18°, pp. 8.

CONSTITUTION and By-Laws of the Albany Gallery of Fine Arts, instituted Nov., 1845.   12°, pp. 12.

CONSTITUTION and By-Laws of the Albany Republican Artillery; founded in 1809, by Col. John Mills; adopted 1809; amended 1844.   18°, pp.

DIXON, JOHN.   Twin Brothers.   12°.
   6,000 copies; the second edition.   Not on file.

DOUGLASS, D. B.   Further Statement of Facts and Circumstances connected with the Removal of the Author from the Presidency of Kenyon College, in answer to the Reply of Trustees, etc.   8°, pp. 71.
   2,000 copies.

FISHER, SAMUEL W.   The Purpose of God in the Early Death of the Christian, illustrated; a Sermon, occasioned by the death of Miss Mary S. Dwight, a Teacher in the Albany Female Academy, delivered in the Fourth Presbyterian Church, Albany, on Sabbath, March 2, 1845. 8°, pp. 32.
   800 copies.

FISHER, SAMUEL W.   The Supremacy of Mind; a Lecture introductory to the eleventh annual course of Lectures before the Young Men's Association of the City of Albany.   8°, pp. 49.
   400 copies.

HOLMES, EDWIN.   Minutes of the Particular Synod of Albany; convened at Hudson, N. Y., May 7, 1845.   8°, pp. 31.
   200 copies.

HOWARD, NATHAN.   Reports of Cases argued and determined in the Supreme Court, at Special Term, with the Points of Practice decided, from October Term, 1844, to September Term, 1845.   Vol. I, 8°, pp. 263.

HUNTINGTON, EZRA A. The House of God, and the Law of the House; a Sermon, preached, at the Dedication of the new House of Worship erected by the Third Presbyterian Church, on Clinton Square, Albany, Wednesday evening, Dec. 3, 1845. 8°, pp. 46.
250 copies.

KIP, WILLIAM INGRAHAM. Two Pastoral Letters addressed to the Congregation of St. Paul's Church, Albany, by their absent rector. 12°, pp. 12.

MEDICUS, [Morgan Lewis.] Principles applied to the Preservation of Health; together with Remarks on the Imagination. 8°, pp. 30.
5,000 copies.

MILLER, GEORGE B. Harmonious Action the Duty of the Church; a Sermon, preached before the New York Ministerium of the Evangelical Lutheran Church, at its semi-centennial Anniversary in Albany, Sept. 7, 1745. 8°, pp. 25.
300 copies.

MINUTES of the Troy Conference of the Methodist Episcopal Church, held at Schenectady, N. Y., May 7, 1845. 12°, pp. 23.
2,500 copies.

MINUTES of the Rensselaerville Baptist Association.
1,000 copies. Not on file.

MUNSELL, JOEL. Webster's Calendar or the Albany Almanac, for the year of our Lord 1846: Being the latter part of the 70th and beginning of the 71st year of the independence of the United States: The 6559th year of the Julian Period: The latter part of the 5606th and beginning of the 5607th year since the creation of the world, according to the Jews: The 2599th year since the foundation of Rome: The 2622d year of the Olympiads of Greece: The latter part of the 1261st, and beginning of the 1262d year since the *hegira*, or flight of Mahomet. 12°, pp. 36.

PAMPHLET relating to the proposed Bridge over the Hudson river.
175 copies. Not on file.

PITCHER, WILLIAM. Grace: a Series of Discourses delivered to the People of his Charge, in the Ref. Prot. Dutch Church of the Boght, A. D., 1844-5. 12°, pp. 176.

POTTER, HORATIO. Remarks in Favor of Free Churches; being part of an Address delivered on the occasion of laying the Corner Stone of a Free Church at Fort Edward, Washington county, N. Y. 8°, pp. 12.
500 copies.

PULPIT SKETCHES, or the Dreams of a Pew Holder. 8°, pp. 36.
500 copies, of which but few were distributed. But I enjoyed a week's imprisonment in the jail for contempt of court, in refusing to answer the question, who was the author.

RAWSON, T. R. Abstract of the Second Annual Report of the City Missionary Society; presented May 3, 1845. 16°, pp. 8.
400 copies.

[SECRET TERMS for Telegraph Reports.] 18°, pp. 20.

SIMMS, JEPTHA R. History of Schoharie County, and Border Wars of
New York; containing also a sketch of the Causes which led to the
American Revolution; and interesting Memoranda of the Mohawk
Valley; together with much other Historical and Miscellaneous matter
never before published, illustrated with more than thirty engravings.
8°, pp. 672.
> 2,000 copies. This is the most remarkable of the county histories in respect to the
> price it will bring in the market. The author sold the edition himself, at $1.75 a copy.
> Second hand copies will now bring $8.

SMITH, J. FERO. The American Lutheran Mission, with an Appeal in its
behalf: being an Address delivered at the Meeting of the General Synod
of the Evangelical Lutheran Church, at Philadelphia, May 16, 1845.
8°, pp. 42; appendix, pp. 18.

SPENCER, JOHN C. Report to the Vestry of St. Peter's Church, Albany,
of the Lay Delegates appointed by them, who attended the Diocesan
Convention of the Protestant Episcopal Church, held at the City of
New York, on the 23d day of Sept., 1845, and continued to the 30th of
the same month. 8°, pp. 32; appendix, pp. 10.
> 1,000 copies.

SPRAGUE, WILLIAM B. An Address, delivered April 11, 1845, in the Second Presbyterian Church, Albany, on occasion of the interment of
Mr. William Davis, Misses Lucinda and Anna Wood, and Miss Mary
Anne Torrey, who perished in the Wreck of the Steam Boat Swallow,
on the evening of the 7th. 8°, pp. 30.
> 500 copies.

THIRTY-FOURTH Annual Report of the Albany Bible Society. 12°, pp. 12.

WATSON, ALEXANDER. A Lecture, delivered April 2d, 1845, before the
Members of the Albany Female Academy, at the close of the Annual
Course on Astronomy. 8°, pp. 30.
> 500 copies.

WILSON, JAMES, & Co. Catalogues of Plants.
> 500 copies. Not on file.

WYCKOFF. Sermon.
> 500 copies. Not on file.

1846.

A MINISTER OF THE GOSPEL. [T. M. Preble.] Two Hundred Stories
and Select Pieces for Children, adapted to lead them to Love and Obey
their Parents, to be kind and obliging to their companions, and merci-
ful to animals; also to remember their Creator. 18°, pp. 234.
> 2,000 copies.

A SYSTEM of Medical Ethics, adopted by the Medical Society of the State
of New York. 8°, pp. 16.
> 100 copies.

BECK, T. R. By-Laws of the New York State Medical Society. 8°, pp.
> 300 copies. Not on file.

BUTTERFIELD, CONSUL W. Lessons in Punctuation, selected from various Authors for the Use of Schools. 18°, pp. 12.
2,000 copies.

BUTTERFIELD, CONSUL W. Constitution and By-Laws of Mechanics' Mutual Protection, No. 15, of the City of Troy. 18°, pp. 22.

CATALOGUE of Assignee's sale of Hardware, on Friday, Sept. 18th, at 10 o'clock, A. M., at store No. 46, State street. J. I. Jones, auctioneer. 8°, pp. 13.

CIRCULAR and Catalogue of the Albany Female Academy, founded A. D. 1814; incorporated Feb. 16, 1821. 8°, pp. 16.

CONSTITUTION of the Annual Convention of Mechanics' Mutual Protections of the State of New York, adopted June 1–4, 1846, and Constitution, By-Laws and Rules of Order of Protection No. 24, of the town of Auburn. 18°, pp. 32.
200 copies.

CONSTITUTIONS, Rules, Resolutions, etc., of the Albany Axe Company, as existing March 2, 1846. 18°, pp. 11.

DEAN, AMOS. An Attempt to present the Claims of Long Lake to the consideration of all those who are in search of Good Land at a Low Price. 8°, pp. 35, and map.

DOX, H. L. Journal of the Ninth Annual Session of the Franckean Evangelic Lutheran Synod, convened at Fordsboro', Montgomery county, N. Y., June 4, 1846. 8°, pp. 31.
500 copies.

EMMONS, E. and A. OSBORN. American Quarterly Journal of Agriculture and Science. Vols. III, IV, V, VI, 8°.
1,000 copies. Portraits and plates.

EMMONS. E. Description of some of the Bones of the Zeuglodon Cetoides of Prof. Owen. 8°, pp. 6.

EMMONS, E. New York and Taconic Systems. 8°, pp. 11.

EXERCISES of the Alumnæ of the Albany Female Academy, on their Fifth Anniversary, July 16, 1846. 8°, pp. 63.
750 copies.

FITCH, ASA. The Hessian Fly, its History, Character, Transformations, and Habits. Originally published in the American Journal of Agriculture and Science. 8°, pp. 63.

HARRIS's Therapeutics and Bathing Circular. 12°, pp. 16.

HARRIS, THOMAS L., and JOHN TANNER. The Gavel, a monthly Periodical, devoted to Odd-Fellowship and General Literature. Vol. II, 8°, pp. 384. Plates.
3,500 copies.

HOLMES, EDWIN. Minutes of the Particular Synod of Albany; convened at Schenectady, May 6, 1846. 8°, pp. 38.
200 copies.

HOWARD, JEROME B.   The Child's First Book of Reading and Drawing. 12°, pp. 96.
  3,000 copies.

HOWARD, NATHANIEL.   Reports of Cases argued and determined in the Supreme Court at Special Term, with the Points of Practice decided, from December Term, 1845, to September Term, 1846. Vol. II, 8°, pp. 304.

LAWYER, JOHN D.   The Distinction of the Word of God against the Traditions of Men ; a Discourse delivered at the Central Conference of Evangelic Lutheran Ministers, held at German Flatts, Herkimer county, N. Y., Sept. 25, 1845. 8°, pp. 28.
  500 copies.

McCALL, H. S.   First Semi-Annual Report of the Albany City and County Lyceum. 8°, pp. 16.

MACFARLANE, ROBERT.   The Mechanics' Mirror, 8°, pp. 298.
  1,000 copies.

MUNSELL, JOEL.   Webster's Calendar or the Albany Almanac, for the year of our Lord 1847: Being the latter part of the 71st and beginning of the 72d year of the independence of the United States: The 6560th year of the Julian Period : The latter part of the 5607th and beginning of the 5608th year since the creation of the world, according to the Jews: The 2600th year since the foundation of Rome : The 2623d year of the Olympiads of Greece: The latter part of the 1263d, and beginning of the 1264th year since the *hegira*, or flight of Mahomet. 12°, pp. 36.

PEPPER, CALVIN, JR.   Manor of Rensselaerwyck. 8°, pp. 34.
  1,500 copies. The author went into the patroon's wood lot and cut down a tree, informing him of it, hoping to provoke a suit for trespass, that would test his title. Nothing came of it.

PORTER, E. S.   The Language of Affliction : a Sermon occasioned by the Death of Adeline Rider, delivered in the Reformed Dutch Church of Chatham, on Sabbath, Feb. 1, 1846. 8°, pp. 23.

RAWSON, T. R.   Abstract of the Third Annual Report of the City Missionary Society, presented May 6, 1846. 16°, pp. 11.

SIMMS, J. R.   The American Spy, or Freedom's Early Sacrifice : a Tale of the Revolution, founded upon Fact. 8°, pp. 63.
  3,000 copies.

SPRAGUE, WILLIAM B.   An Address delivered at the opening of the Brooklyn Female Academy, on Monday evening, May 4, 1846. 8°, pp. 26.
  1,000 copies.

SPRAGUE, WILLIAM B.   A Sermon, delivered on Sabbath Morning, Jan. 4, 1846, containing Sketches of the History of the Second Presbyterian Church and Congregation, Albany, during thirty years from the period of their organization. 8°, pp. 43.
  500 copies.

SPRAGUE, WILLIAM B.   Letters on Practical Subjects to a Daughter. 12° pp. 305.
  1,000 copies.

SPRAGUE, WILLIAM B.   Sow Well and Reap Well.   12°, pp.
500 copies.

SPRAGUE, WILLIAM B.   Letters to Young Men, founded on the History
of Joseph.   12°, pp. 275.
1,000 copies.

THE ARTICLES of Faith, Discipline, and Standing Resolutions of the
Evangelic Lutheran Churches of West Sandlake and Schodack, adopted
1846.   18°, pp. 18.
500 copies.

THE CONSTITUTION of the State of New York, as Revised by the Convention of 1846.   8°, pp. 16.

THE FANCY BALL: a Letter lost from the Portfolio of a young Lady of
Albany.   8°, pp. 28.
1,000 copies.

THIRTY-FIFTH Annual Report of the Albany County Bible Society.   12°,
pp. 12.

VAN VOORST, HOOPER C.   An Oration occasioned by the Death of Henry
White, delivered before the Theta Chapter of the Upsilon Society,
Union College, July, 1845.   8°, pp. 20, appendix 3.

1847.

BATTEL, MELLEN.   A Plan and Constitution for a Depository and Sale
of American Mechanic Arts, Science and Manufactures.   12°, pp. 26.
Frontispiece.
500 copies.

BOYNTON, B. H.   Mysteries of Troy.   8°, pp. 40.
2,500 copies.   Not on file.

BRITAIN, S. B.   A Discourse on War, or the Duties and Obligations of
the Individual, as connected with the Rights of the Civil Government;
delivered on Sunday morning, April 3, 1847.   8°, pp. 20.
750 copies.

CHARTER of the Young Men's Association for Mutual Improvement in
the City of Albany ; together with the Rules and Regulations adopted
and revised by the executive committee, for the Government of the
Association in the several departments, Feb. 7, 1847.   8°, pp. 19.

CLERICUS.   [George H. Thacher.]   A Letter to the Synod of Albany, on
the Subject of Dancing: wherein is discussed the Question, ought the
Synod to take action on this Subject, which shall bind the Conscience
of the Church ?   8°, pp. 30.

COLUMBUS and his Times.
2d edition.   1,000 copies.

DIXON, JOHN.   The Twin Brothers; being the Lives of John and James
Dixon, born at Naworth Park, Cumberland, England.   12°, pp. 72.
6,000 copies.

EMMONS, E., and A. OSBORN.   American Quarterly Journal of Agriculture and Science.   Vols. V, VI.   8°.
2,000 copies.   Portraits and plates.

FITCH, ASA.   Winter Insects.   8°, pp.
200 copies.   Made up from Emmons's Ag. Journal.   Not on file.

FREE THINKER.   [A. B. Crocker.]   Random Sketches upon Witches,
Dreams, Love and Romance.   8°, pp. 16.
3,000 copies.   A foolish performance by a country Presbyterian preacher.

HALDEMAN, S. S.   A Description of several New and Interesting Animals,
communicated for the American Journal of Agriculture and Science.
8°, pp. 7.

HALLEY, EBENEZER.   Christianity ; its past struggles ; its present position ;
its future prospects ; an Address, delivered before the Theological Society at Union College, on Sabbath Evening, July 25, 1847.   8°, pp. 39.
500 copies.

HOLMES, EDWIN.   Minutes of the Particular Synod of Albany.   8°, pp. 27.
200 copies.   Not on file.

McCALL, JOHN.   Address delivered before the New York State Medical
Society, in the Assembly Chamber of the Capitol, at the City of Albany,
Feb. 2, 1847.   8°, pp. 17.
200 copies.

McCALL, JOHN.   Dissertation delivered before the New York State Medical Society, in the Assembly Chamber of the Capitol, at the City of
Albany, Feb. 2, 1847.   8°, pp. 20.
200 copies.

MINUTES of the Troy Conference of the Methodist Episcopal Church, held
at Albany, May 6, 1847.   12°, pp. 23.
3,000 copies.

MUNSELL, JOEL.   Webster's Calendar, or the Albany Almanac, for the
year of our Lord 1848 : Being the latter part of the 72d and beginning
of the 73d year of the independence of the United States : The 6561st
year of the Julian Period : The latter part of the 5608th and beginning
of the 5609th year since the creation of the world, according to the
Jews : The 2601st year since the foundation of Rome : The 2624th year
of the Olympiads of Greece : The latter part of the 1264th, and beginning of the 1265th year since the *hegira*, or flight of Mahomet.   12°, pp. 36.

PEASE, FREDERICK S.   An Account of the Descendants of John Pease,
who landed at Martha's Vineyard in the year 1632.   12°, pp. 52.
250 copies.

PREBLE, THOMAS M.   The Voice of God : or, an Account of the Unpara-
lelled Fires, Hurricanes, Floods and Earthquakes, commencing with
1845 : also, some Account of Pestilence, Famine, and increase of Crime.
12°, pp. 84.
3,000 copies.   Written to show that these calamities were the result of the wicked-
ness of the times.   The author was a Second Advent preacher, in haste to bring the
world to a close.

Rawson, T. R.   Fourth Annual Report of the Albany City Missionary Society, presented May 7, 1847.   16°, pp. 16.

Schoolcraft, Henry R.   Notes on the Iroquois; or Contributions to American History, Antiquities, and General Ethnology.   8°, pp. xv, 498.
1,000 copies. This was originally published as a legislative document. I was struck with the interest attached to the subject, and proposed its republication to E. H. Pease, not yet having attempted to publish anything myself. The work owes its existence in this form to my persuasion. Portraits and wood-cuts.

Sprague, William B.   A Discourse commemorative of the Rev. Thomas Chalmers, D. D., delivered in the Second Presbyterian Church in Albany, on Sabbath evening, June 27, 1847; with a Letter from Dr. Chalmers to an American Clergyman.   8°, pp. 47.
600 copies.

Sprague, William B.   An Address, delivered on the Evening of the Twenty-second of February, MDCCCXLVII, before the Young Men's Association of the City of Albany.   8°, pp. 51.
600 copies.

Sweet's Elocution.
1,000 copies.   Not on file.

The Parthenon.   Nos. 2, 3, 4.
Lacks No. 1; was edited by the students of Union College.

Thirty sixth Annual Report of the Albany County Bible Society   12°, pp. 12.
1,000 copies.

Winegar, R.   Minutes of the Fifty-first Anniversary of the Rensselaerville Baptist Association, held in the Meeting House of the Baptist Church in Charleston, Montgomery county, N. Y., Wednesday and Thursday, Sept. 15, 16, 1847.   12°, pp. 16.
900 copies.

1848.

Adam, William.   Genealogy of the Adam Family.   12°, pp. 16.
110 copies.

Administrators' Sale of the Estate of the late Jacob Hochstrasser.   8°, pp. 15.

Articles of Association of the Albany and Saratoga Plank Road Company.   8°, pp. 4.

Barrett, Solomon.   The Principles of Grammar: being a Compendious Treatise on the Languages, English, Latin and Greek; founded on the immutable principle of the relation which one word sustains to another.   12°, pp. 204.
800 copies.

Bement, Caleb N.   American Journal of Agriculture and Science, devoted to the promotion of Agriculture, Horticulture, Science, Arts, and Industry.   8°, pp. 576.   Woodcuts.
1,250 copies.

BLATCHFORD, THOMAS W. Two Addresses before the Medical Society of the State of New York, in Session at Albany, Feb. 1 and 2, 1848. 8°, pp. 28.
    500 copies.

BUCKMINSTER, J. S. Extract from a Discourse preached in the Church in Brattle Square, Boston, October, 1811, the Sabbath after the interment of the Hon. James Bowdoin. 8°, pp. 8.
    150 copies. This was printed for the Rev. Dr. Sprague.

CINDERELLA, or the Little Glass Slipper. 12°, pp. 8.

CIRCULAR and Catalogue of Mrs. Brinckerhoof's Boarding and Day School for Young Ladies, No. 112 State street, Albany. 12°, pp. 8.

CIRCULAR and Catalogue of the Albany Female Academy, founded A. D. 1814 ; incorporated Feb. 16, 1821. 8°, pp. 20.
    1,500 copies.

CIRCULAR and Catalogue of the Albany Medical College. 8°, pp.
    700 copies. Not on file.

CIRCULAR and Catalogue of the S. S. Seward Institute, at Florida, Orange county, N. Y. ; under the care of Elizabeth Parsons ; founded 1845 ; incorporated 1847. 8°, pp. 10.
    300 copies.

COLE, WILLIAM K. The Odd-Fellow's Magazine. 8°, pp. 224. Portraits on steel.
    3,000 copies.

CONFESSION of Faith of the Second Baptist Church of Galway, Saratoga county, N. Y. 16°, pp. 18.

CONSTITUTION and By-Laws of Albany Temple of Honor. 18°, pp. 16.
    300 copies.

CONSTITUTION and By-Laws of Albany Division No. 24, of the Sons of Temperance of the State of New York. 18°, pp. 32.
    1,500 copies.

CONSTITUTION and By-Laws of Coeymans Division No. ... of the Sons of Temperance of the State of New York, etc. 18°, pp.
    500 copies.

CONSTITUTION and By-Laws of Vesta Division of the Sons of Temperance of the State of New York, etc. 18°, pp.
    500 copies.

CONSTITUTION and By-Laws of Eagle Division No. 306, of the Sons of Temperance of the State of New York ; approved by the Grand Division, April 4, 1848. 18°, pp. 26.
    200 copies.

CONSTITUTION and By-Laws of Greenville Division, No. 361, of the Sons of Temperance of the State of New York ; instituted May 20, 1848 18°, pp. 32.
    500 copies.

CONSTITUTION, By-Laws and Rules of Order, of Scho-negh-ta-da Lodge. No. 356, I. O. O. F., of the State of New York, located at Albany ; organized March, 1848. 18°, pp. 36.
    300 copies.

CONSTITUTION of the Right Worthy Grand Encampment of Patriarchs of the State of New York, and the Constitution, By-Laws, and Rules of Order of En-Hakkore Encampment of Patriarchs, No. 5, I. O. of O. F., of the City of Albany, N. Y. 16°, pp. 64.
300 copies.

CROCKER, REV. A. B. Pedo Baptist. pp. 24.
1,000 copies. Not on file.

DEAN, AMOS. Introductory Lecture, delivered before the Free Lecture Department of the Young Men's Association, Albany, Dec. 7, 1848. 8°, pp. 30.
500 copies.

ELIZABETH, CHARLOTTE. Alice Benden, or the Borrowed Shilling; and other Tales. 18°, pp. 177.
500 copies.

ELIZABETH, CHARLOTTE. Glimpses of the Past, or the Museum. 18°, pp. 228.
500 copies.

ELIZABETH, CHARLOTTE. Philip and his Garden; and other Tales suitable for Sabbath Schools. 18°, pp.
500 copies.

ELIZABETH, CHARLOTTE. Fortune Teller.
500 copies.

ELIZABETH, CHARLOTTE. The Flower of Innocence, or Rachel; a True Narrative, with other Tales. 18°, pp. 189.
500 copies.

ELIZABETH, CHARLOTTE. The Simple Flower, and other Tales. 18°, pp. 166.
500 copies.

ELIZABETH, CHARLOTTE. Tales and Illustrations.
500 copies.

HEERMANCE, JOHN C. Despatch Air-Tight Cooking Stove. 12°, pp. 12.
2,000 copies.

HISTORY of Little Red Riding Hood. 12°, pp. 8.

HOLGATE, JEROME B. American Genealogy, being a History of some of the Early Settlers of North America, and their Descendants, from their first emigration to the present time, with their Intermarriages and Collateral Branches, including notices of prominent families and distinguished individuals, with anecdotes, reminiscences, traditions, sketches of the founding of cities, villages, manors, and progressive improvements of the country, from its wilderness state to the present era. Illustrated by Genealogical Tables. 4°, pp. 248.
250 copies.

HOLMES, EDWIN. Minutes of the Particular Synod of Albany, convened at West Troy, N. Y., May 3, 1848. 8°, pp. 35.
200 copies.

HORTON, H. P. A Digest of the Militia Law of the State of New York, with copious Forms adapted to every case. 8°, pp. 40.
3,000 copies.

HOWARD, JEROME B.   Reading and Drawing Book.   12°, pp. 96.
   2,000 copies.

HUNTINGTON, E. A.   A Funeral Discourse, on David Perkins Page, A. M.,
   late Principal of the State Normal School, Albany, delivered Sunday
   evening, Jan. 9, 1848, before the Executive Committee, the Faculty and·
   Pupils of the School.   8°, pp. 39.
   500 copies.

HUNT, WILLIAM.   Hunt's Albany Commercial Directory for 1848-9.   12°,
   pp. 156, supplement 32.
   500 copies.

HUNT, WILLIAM.   Leaves from the American Biographical Sketch Book.
   [Sketch of Emma Willard.]   8°, pp. 9.

HUNT, WILLIAM.   The American Biographical Sketch Book.   8°, pp. 408.
   Portraits on wood.
   500 copies.

LOVECHILD, MISS.   The Ladder to Learning.   12°, pp. 8.

MACDONALD, A. J.   Monuments, Grave Stones, Burying Grounds, Ceme-
   teries, Temples, etc.   12°, pp. 22.
   500 copies.

MEMBERS of Hope Lodge, No. 3.   18°, pp. 7.

MENAND.   Catalogue of Plants.   12°, pp. 19.

MUNSELL, JOEL.   Select Stories for Children, designed for their Moral and
   Religious Improvement.   18°, pp. 180.
   2,000 copies. A compilation.

MUNSELL, JOEL.   Webster's Calendar or the Albany Almanac, for the
   year of our Lord 1849: Being the latter part of the 73d and beginning
   of the 74th year of the independence of the United States: 6562d year
   of the Julian Period: The latter part of the 5609th and beginning of
   the 5610th year since the creation of the world, according to the Jews:
   The 2602d year since the foundation of Rome: The 2625th year of the
   Olympiads of Greece: The latter part of the 1265th, and beginning of
   the 1266th year since the *hegira*, or flight of Mahomet.   12°, pp. 36.

NAIRNE, CHARLES MURRAY.   Atheism and Pantheism, a Lecture delivered
   before the Young Men's Association for Mutual Improvement in the
   City of Albany, on Friday evening, March 10, 1848.   8°, pp. 54.
   1,000 copies.

OLD DAME Trot and her Comical Cat.   12°, pp. 8.

OUTLINES of the Life and Character of Lewis Cass.   8°, pp. 64.
   5,100 copies.

PEASE, FREDERICK S.   Genealogy of the Ancestors and Posterity of Isaac
   Lawrence.   12°, pp. 20.
   200 copies.

PETERS, ABSALOM.   Sprinkling the only Mode of Baptism made known
   in the Scriptures ; and the Scripture Warrant for Infant Baptism.   18°,
   pp. 184.
   1,000 copies.

PETITIONERS for Recharter, and Officers and Members of Hope Lodge, No. 3, I. O. O. F. 32°, pp. 7.

PRUYN, SAMUEL. Brief Account of the Albany County Penitentiary. 8°, pp. 6. Woodcut.

RAWSON, T. R. City Missionary Society; abstract from the Fifth Annual Report, presented May 6, 1848. 12°, pp. 12.

REPORT of the Thirty-fifth Annual Examination of the Albany Female Academy, and of the Exercises of the Alumnæ of the Institution, on their Seventh Anniversary, July, 1848. 8°, pp. 16.
1,500 copies.

RICH, REUBEN. Patent Water Wheels. 12°, pp. 24.
1,000 copies.

SALISBURY, J. H. Examination of five Varieties of Cabbage. 8°, pp. 11.
100 copies.

SHARTS, JOHN. Eulogy on the Death of the late Captain Abram Van Olinda, who fell at the Battle of Chapultepec, Sept. 13, 1847, delivered in the First Presbyterian Church, Albany, on Friday, July 7, 1848. 8°, pp. 24.
1,000 copies.

SMITH, REUBEN. Recollections of Nettleton, and the Great Revival of 1820. 18°, pp. 150.
1,000 copies.

SMITH, THOMAS. Walker's Critical Pronouncing Dictionary and Expositor of the English Language, abridged; in which not only the meaning of every word is explained, and the sound of every syllable distinctly shown, but where words are subject to different pronunciations, the best pronunciation is selected; also containing a table of the simple and dipthongal vowels, referred to by the figures over the letters in this Dictionary. 16°, pp. 411.

SPEECH of the Hon. R. D. Davis, of Dutchess, at the Great Democratic Ratification Meeting, at the Capitol, on Tuesday evening, Sept. 26, 1848; also Speech of Gen. Shields, at Cleveland. 8°, pp. 8.
2,000 copies.

SPRAGUE, T. DWIGHT. The American Literary Magazine. 2 vols., 8°. Portraits on steel.
3,000 copies.

SPRAGUE, WILLIAM B. An Address, delivered before the Literary Societies of the Wesleyan University, Middletown, Conn., July 31, 1848. 8°, pp. 56.
600 copies.

SPRAGUE, W. B. Letters to Young Men.
500 copies. Not on file.

STATE of New York: Substitute for Senate Bill No. 210. An Act concerning Passengers coming to the City of New York. 8°, pp. 8.

STEELE, JOHN B.   The Symbol and Word of Encouragement to the Build-
ers of the Spiritual Temple: a Sermon, preached at the Ordination and
Installation of Rev. Richard H. Steele, as Pastor over the Presbyterian
Church of Freehold, in Charlton, Saratoga county, N. Y., February 16,
1848.   8°, pp. 35.
   500 copies.

SWEET'S Elocution.
   1,000 copies.

THE ADVENTURES of Mother Hubbard and her Dog.   12°, pp. 8.

THE DIVERTING History of John Gilpin.   12°, pp. 8.

THE ENTERTAINING History of Whittington and his Cat.   12°, pp. 8.

THE HISTORY of Goody Two Shoes.   12°, pp. 8.

THE HISTORY of Little Dame Crump and her Little White Pig.   12°, pp. 8.

THE HISTORY of the Children in the Wood.   12°, pp. 8.

THE HOUSE that Jack Built.   12°, pp. 8.

THE LIFE and Death of Cock Robin.   12°, pp. 8.

THIRTY-SEVENTH Annual Report of the Albany County Bible Society.
   12°, pp. 11.
   1,000 copies.

TILLINGHAST, JOHN L.   Some Account of Acts in relation to the Construction of the Albany Basin, with the Opinion of a Member of the
Albany Bar, as to the Rights of Parties interested.   8°, pp. 35.
   200 copies.

TOWNSEND, FRANKLIN, & Co.   Pattern List.   12°, pp. 153.
   250 copies.

WINEGAR, R.   Minutes of the Forty-second Anniversary of the Rensselaerville Baptist Association, held with the Baptist Church in Rensselaerville, Sept. 20, 1848.   12°, pp. 12.

[WOODS, LEONARD.]   Sermons by the late Rev. James Richards, D.D.;
with an Essay on his Character, by William B. Sprague, D.D.   12°, pp.
387.
   1,000 copies.

1849.

ALBANY Board of Underwriters.
   150 copies.   Not on file.

ANNUAL CATALOGUE of the Officers and Students of Hartwick Theological
and Classical Seminary, August, 1849.   8°, pp. 8.
   300 copies.

ANNUAL REPORT Albany Female Academy.   8°, pp. 10.
   1,000 copies.   Not on file.

BARNARD, DANIEL D. A Discourse on the Life, Character and Public Services of Ambrose Spencer, late Chief Justice of the Supreme Court of the State of New York; delivered by request before the Bar of the City of Albany, Jan. 5, 1849. 8°, pp. 104.
1,450 copies.

BEATTIE, ROBERT H. A Discourse on the Millennial State of the Church, prepared by appointment of the Synod of Albany, and delivered before that body, Oct. 11, 1849. 8°, pp. 51.
1,000 copies.

CATALOGUE of Hardware for Sale by Pruyn & Vosburgh, 39 State street, Albany, N. Y. 24°, pp. 24.

CODE of Procedure of the State of New York; as amended by the Legislature, by an act passed April, 1849. 8°, pp. 144.
1,500 copies.

DOX, H. L. Christ the Foundation: a Synodical and Dedicatory Discourse, delivered at Gardnersville, Schoharie county, N. Y., June 7th, 1849. 8°, pp. 42.

ELIZABETH, CHARLOTTE. Humility before Honor, and other Tales and Illustrations, with a Brief Memoir of the Author, by Wm. B. Sprague. 18°, pp. 195.

FURNESS, WM. H. A Sermon on the True Nature of Worship, preached Sunday, Feb. 11th, 1849, at the Church of the Messiah, New York. 8°, pp. 8.

HEYES, HENRY. Hymns and other Sacred Pieces in Verse. 18°, pp. 123.
Mr. Heyes was a Methodist preacher from England. He did not have money to pay for the printing and binding, and after a vain effort to sell his sacred pieces, he came to me to say that he was going back to his own country, and expressed much regret at his inability to pay his bill. He seemed to regard the apology as equivalent to cash, and having unburdened his mind, such a serenity settled upon his countenance, I did not hint that his tender was below par, and he departed in peace.

HOLMES, EDWIN. Minutes of the Particular Synod of Albany, convened at Albany, N. Y., May 2, 1849. 8°, pp. 30.
200 copies.

HOLMES, EDWIN. A Sermon occasioned by the Death of the Rev. Peter S. Wynkoop, pastor of the Reformed Dutch Church of Bloomingrove, who died at Hudson, Nov. 1, 1848; preached in the Reformed Dutch Church of Hudson, Nov. 3, 1848. 8°, pp. 31.
200 copies.

HOWARD, NATHAN, JR. Practice Reports in the Supreme Court and Court of Appeals. Vol. IV, 8°, pp, iv, 484.

HOWARD, NATHAN. Reports of Cases of Practice decided by the Supreme Court and Court of Appeals, since the Organization of the Judiciary under the Amended Constitution of 1846, and in pursuance of the Judiciary Act of 1847, and the Code of Procedure which became a law on the first day of July, 1848, except the first fifty pages, which are cases decided by the old Supreme Court, from Sept., 1846, to March, 1849. 8°, pp. 451.

Hun, Thomas. Medical Systems, Medical Science and Empiricism; an Introductory Lecture, before the Albany Medical College, delivered Oct. 3, 1848. 8°, pp. 46.

500 copies.

Hunt, William. American Biographical Panorama. 8°, pp. 480.

1,000 copies. Portraits and plates. The author had been engaged some time at Washington, as a reporter ; but fancying that he was overworked, he came to Albany to recreate, and undertook publishing. He entertained a theory that the public called for quantity rather than quality, and in his sketches of individuals, when he lacked facts, he eked out the desired quantity from a store of scraps of sentimental prose and verse, which he had gathered for that or some other purpose. In this volume he gives a sketch of each of the signers of the Declaration of Independence, and being desirous of having portraits to accompany the sketches, he gave a young English engraver just arrived, a *carte blanche* to produce all of them on wood. Thus commissioned he took a room in Commercial Building, furnished it with a barrel of ale and a quantity of tobacco pipes, and under the inspiration imparted by these, produced for the first time, portraits of all the signers ! Mr. Hunt quickly disposed of his carefully saved earnings as a reporter, and returned to Washington, where he soon after died.

III. Chronicles. 8°, pp. 8.

Kennedy, Duncan. A Sermon delivered May 6, 1849, in the North Dutch Church, Albany, on occasion of the lamented Death of the Rev. William J. Pohlman, late Missionary to China, and with some modification, on June 10th, in the City of New York, as the Annual Missionary Discourse before the General Synod of the Reformed Dutch Church. 8°, pp. 46.

500 copies.

Kip, Wm. I. A Few Days at Nashotah. 8°, pp. 31.

1,000 copies.

Law to amend the Law entitled a Law to amend Chapter xxxv of the City Laws entitled of the Erection of Wooden Buildings, passed Aug. 6, 1849. 8°, pp. 4.

Mark's Toys. 12°.

14,400 copies.

Munsell, Joel. The Albany Annual Register, for 1849; containing a Directory to the Places of Business and Public Institutions, Contributions to the History and Antiquities of the City, and other Matters of Interest. 12°, pp. 181.

500 copies. Plates and maps.

Munsell, Joel. Webster's Calendar or the Albany Almanac, for the year of our Lord 1850: Being the latter part of the 74th and beginning of the 75th year of the independence of the United States : The 6563d year of the Julian Period : The latter part of the 5610th and beginning of the 5611th year since the creation of the world, according to the Jews : The 2603d year since the foundation of Rome : The 2626th year of the Olympiads of Greece : The latter part of the 1266th, and beginning of the 1267th year since the *hegira*, or flight of Mahomet. 12°, pp. 36.

Potter, Horatio. Christian Suffering : its Dignity and its Efficacy : a Sermon occasioned by the Death of the Hon. Ambrose Spencer, and preached in St. Peter's Church, Albany, on Sunday, March 19, 1848. 8°, pp. 16.

50 copies.

PRUYN, SAMUEL. Biographical Sketch of Amos Pilsbury, and a Brief Account of the Albany Penitentiary. 8°, pp. 24.
200 copies. Woodcuts.

RAWSON, T. R. City Missionary Society: abstract from the Sixth Annual Report, presented May 7, 1849. 12°.
500 copies.

REMARKS on the Attorney-General's Report to the Senate. 12°, pp. 7.

REMONSTRANCE of two of the Directors of the Caughnawaga Bridge Company, against the proposed Law to Repeal or Modify the Act incorporating said Company. 8°, pp. 7.

REPORT of the Attorney-General on the Constitutionality of erecting the new counties of Patterson and Unadilla from parts of different Senate and Assembly Districts. 8°, pp. 4.

REPORT of the Select Committee of the Senate, showing the Frauds and Peculations of Edwin Croswell, Theodore Olcott, John L. Crew and others, by which the Canal Bank was ruined. 8°, pp. 64.
3,000 copies. This was printed at the expense of Mr. Henry H. Van Dyk, who entertained this style of sympathy for Mr. Croswell.

RICHARDS, JAMES. Sermons by the late Rev. James Richards, D.D., with an Essay on his Character by Wm. B. Sprague, D.D. 12°, pp. 387.

ROBINSON, H. N. A Treatise on Astronomy, descriptive, physical and practical. Designed for Schools, Colleges, and Private Students. 8°, pp. ix, 302, 54.

RULES, Regulations and By-Laws, for the Government and Discipline of the Albany County Penitentiary. 8°, pp. 18.

SCHAEFFER, CHARLES F. Minutes of the Fifty-fourth Synod of the Evangelical Lutheran Ministerium of the State of New York, and adjacent States and Countries, held at Valatie, Columbia County, N. Y., September 1, 1849, and the following days. 8°, pp. 27.
500 copies.

SPENCER, JOHN C. Memorial of Ambrose Spencer, formerly Chief Justice of the Supreme Court of the State of New York : consisting of Proceedings of Public Bodies and Meetings, and of Sermons and Addresses on the occasion of his Death, and in illustration of his Life and Character. 8°, pp. 78, 104.
500 copies. Portrait.

SPENCER, JOHN C. Report to the Vestry of St. Peter's Church, Albany, of their Delegate to the Diocesan Convention, held at New York, September, 1849. 8°, pp. 8.
200 copies.

SPRAGUE, WILLIAM B. A Discourse commemorative of the late Ambrose Spencer, late Chief Justice of the State of New York ; delivered in the Second Presbyterian Church, Albany, on Sabbath evening, April 20, 1848. 8°, pp. 34.
50 copies.

STARTLING, Thrilling and Interesting Narrative of the Life, Sufferings, Singular and Surprising Adventures of Fanny Templeton Danforth, who, disguised in the Uniform of a Midshipman, went in search of her Lover, an Officer in the United States Navy, and was taken Prisoner by the pirate ship Demon of the Seas, May 17, 1848, and was rescued by the crew of the United States Man of War Macedonian, led on by her Lover, just as she was to have been burned alive by her captors, the pirates of the Isle of Pines. 8°, pp. 36.

STEELE, GEORGE B.   The Annual Report of the President of the Young Men's Association of the City of Albany, made at its Sixteenth Annual Meeting, Feb., 1848.   8°, pp. 20.
    250 copies.

STEVENS, ALEXANDER H.   The Plea of Humanity in behalf of Medical Education ; the Annual Address delivered before the New York State Medical Society, and Members of the Legislature, at the Capitol, Feb. 6, 1849.   8°, pp. 20.
    2,500 copies.

THIRTY-EIGHTH Annual Report of the Albany County Bible Society.   12°, pp. 12.
    1,000 copies.

TRIAL of Mrs. Margaret Howard, for the Murder of Miss Mary Ellen Smith, her husband's paramour, in Cincinnati, on the 2d of February last.   8°, pp. 64.
    4,000 copies.

WATSON, ALEXANDER.   Circular of the Kinderhook Academy.   12°, pp. 8.
    200 copies.   2d edition, 8vo, pp. 8, 300 copies.

WHIG or Abolition ? that's the Question.   8°, pp. 5.
    250 copies.

1850.

ALBANY State Register.   Folio.
    Daily paper, published by an association of the friends of Millard Fillmore, to advocate his nomination for president of the United States.   Edited by Alexander Seward, and Jerome C. Fuller.

ANNUAL Catalogue of the Officers and Students of Hartwick Theological and Classical Seminary, for the Academical year, 1849–50.   12°, pp. 9.
    250 copies.

BEMENT, C. N.   Hints from Cousin Susan's Recipe Book.   12°, pp. 24.
    1,000 copies.

BY-LAWS and Prospectus of the Empire State Mutual Health Association, at West Galway, N. Y., adopted October, 1850.   12°, pp. 12.

CATALOGUE of the Books in the Library of the Rensselaer Street Mission Sunday School, Feb. 2, 1850.   18°, pp. 17.

CATALOGUE and Circular of the Albany Female Academy.   8°, pp. 20.
    1,500 copies.   Not on file.

COLLIER, JOHN A. Fete Extraordinary ! Martin Van Buren's Last Supper. 12°, pp. 11.

COMSTOCK, GEORGE F. Reports of Cases argued and determined in the Court of Appeals of the State of New York. Vol. II. 8°, pp. 613.
2,000 copies.

CONE, SOLOMON. (?) Music.
1,700 copies. Not on file.

CONSTITUTION and By-Laws of Tivoli Temple of Honor, No. 22, of the State of New York ; organized March, 1826. 18°, pp. 18.

CONSTITUTION, By-Laws and Rules of Greenville Lodge, No. 394, I. O. of O. F. of the State of New York, held in the Village of Greenville, Greene county. 16°, pp. 42.

CUYLER, JACOB C. Trial of Reuben Dunbar, for the Murder of Stephen V. Lester and David L. Lester, eight and ten years of age, in the Town of Westerlo, on Saturday, Sept. 28, 1850. 8°, pp. 75.
2,000 copies.

DICKERMAN, JAIRUS. Troy Steam Mill, No. 37 Ferry street. 12°, pp. 8.

EMMONS, E. Strictures of E. Emmons, upon certain parts of the Report of the Select Committee appointed to investigate matters connected with the publication of the State Work on Natural History. 8°, pp. 14.
300 copies.

FONDEY, JOHN. A Medical Tract for the Ministry and the People. 12°, pp. 4.

FOSTER, J. T. Introduction to the Study of Geology ; together with a Key to Foster's Geological Chart. 18°, pp. 137.
300 copies.

GROESBEECK, STEPHEN. Rates of Premium and Classes of Hazard adopted by the Fire Insurance Companies doing Business in the City of Albany. 12°, pp. 8.

HALLEY, EBENEZER. The Pantheism of Germany : a Sermon delivered before the Synod of Albany, at Saratoga Springs, October 9, 1850. 8°, pp. 64.
500 copies.

HOLMES, EDWIN. Minutes of the Particular Synod of Albany, convened at Schenectady, May 1, 1850. 8°, pp. 33.
200 copies.

HUSBANDS, JOSEPH D. and HORACE LATHROP, JR. Addresses delivered at the Thirty-fifth Commencement of Hartwick Seminary, Otsego county, N. Y., August 27th and 28th, 1850. 8°, pp. 37.
500 copies.

ILLUSTRATED Book of Stoves manufactured by Vose & Co., Albany, N. Y. 4°, pp. 90.

JACKSON, J. W. Elements of Conic Sections. 8°, pp. 96.
600 copies. Diagrams.

KENYON, H. B. Backus and Kenyon on Secret Societies : being a Discourse delivered by Rev. J. S. Backus, of Auburn, and a Reply to the same by Rev. H. B. Kenyon, of Ira, Cayuga county, N. Y. 12°, pp. 44, 52, and xiv.

KIP, LEONARD.   California Sketches, with Recollections of Gold Mines.
12°, pp. 57.
1,000 copies.

LAWS of the State of New York, passed at the Seventy-third Session of the
Legislature, begun the first day of January, and ended the tenth day of
April, 1850, at the City of Albany, with Marginal Notes and a General
Index, and the Names of Residences of the Judges and Surrogates,
County Clerks, Sheriffs, and District Attorneys of the State of New
York.   8°, pp. 871.
5,000 copies.

LEAKE, ISAAC Q.   Memoir of the Life and Times of General John Lamb,
an Officer of the Revolution, who commanded the Post at West Point
at the time of Arnold's defection, and his Correspondence with Washington, Clinton, Patrick Henry, and other distinguished Men of his
Time.   8vo, pp. x, 431.
1,000 copies. Portrait and maps. General Anthony Lamb, the son of Gen. John
Lamb, was desirous that his father's exploits in the Revolution should be commemo-
rated in a book, and his brother-in-law, Isaac Q. Leake, undertook, from the family
papers and other sources, to prepare this memorial volume. The family was parsi-
monious of money, and Leake was furnished with a capital of $380 only, with which
to procure an engraved portrait and have the printing done. The interest in General
Lamb was not sufficient to create a brisk sale, and the work, therefore, did not pay.
An effort was made to sell the edition to Gen. Anthony for the debt remaining upon
it, but without effect.

LIST of Officers and Members of Hope Lodge No. 1, I. O. of O. F., Albany,
July 1, 1850.   18°, pp. 6.
100 copies. This was the oldest lodge of Odd-Fellows in the state.

MUNSELL, JOEL.   The Typographical Miscellany.   8°, pp. 268.
200 copies, published in numbers. Woodcuts. This was begun with the view of
collecting the history of printing in the State of New York by counties. The cooperation of printers was expected in so interesting a subject. But it was found
that many printers kept no files of their papers, and had no knowledge of their
predecessors, nor did they entertain any disposition to aid such an enterprise. The
original plan was soon abandoned as impracticable, and a diversion made in the
scope of the work.

MUNSELL, JOEL.   Catalogue Sale of Rare and Valuable Works belonging
to a Private Library.   Clark & Jones will sell on Wednesday evening,
March 20, 1850, etc.   8°, pp. 16.

MUNSELL, JOEL.   The Albany Annual Register for 1850; containing a
Directory to the Places of Business and Public Institutions, Contributions to the History and Antiquities of the City, and other Matters of
Interest.   12°, pp. 184.
500 copies. This failing to get patronage, the two years were united, with a portion of new matter, and omission of some ephemeral articles, and formed the first
volume of the *Annals of Albany*.

MUNSELL, JOEL.   The Annals of Albany.   Vol. I.   12°, pp. 377.

MUNSELL, JOEL.   The Annals of Albany.   Vol. II.   12°, pp. 312.

MUNSELL, JOEL. Webster's Calendar, or the Albany Almanac, for the year of our Lord 1851 : Being the latter part of the 75th and beginning of the 76th year of the independence of the United States : The 6564th year of the Julian Period : The latter part of the 5611th and beginning of the 5612th year since the creation of the world, according to the Jews : The 2604th year since the foundation of Rome : The 2627th year of the Olympiads of Greece : The latter part of the 1267th, and beginning of the 1268th year since the *hegira* or flight of Mahomet. 12°, pp. 36.

NATIONAL School Book Series. Fourth Book of Lessons for Schools. Authorized by the Board of Education. 12°, pp. 344.
> 1,000 copies. There were two other educational books in this series, neither of them on file. They were printed for the Canada market.

NORTON, JOHN P. Elements of Scientific Agriculture, or the Connection between Science and the Art of Practical Farming : Prize Essay of the New York State Agricultural Society. 12°, pp. 208.
> 2,000 copies.

PALMER, RAY. A Sermon on the Aim and Method of the Preacher ; delivered on Sabbath morning, Dec. 15, 1850, in the First Congregational Church, Albany. 8°, pp. 30.

PARSONS, LEVI. The Consolations of Surviving Friends, on the Death of a Just Man : a Sermon at the Funeral of Mr. Samuel Rhoades, in the Presbyterian Church, at Skeneateles, Onondaga county, N. Y., March 31, 1850. 8°, pp. 20.

PATERSON, JOHN. The Calculus of Operations. 8°, pp. 184.
> 140 copies. Diagrams.

PATERSON, JOHN. Violin Preceptor. Oblong 4°, pp.
> 2,000 copies.

PATERSON, JOHN. Flute Preceptor.

RAWSON, T. R. Seventh Annual Report of the Albany City Missionary Society, presented May 4, 1850. 12°, pp. 14.
> 500 copies.

REMARKS on the Attorney-General's Report to the Senate. 12°, pp. 7.

RICH, REUBEN. Pressure Center-Vent Water Wheels and Scrolls. 12°, pp. 26.

SCHAEFFER, CHARLES F. Minutes of the Fifty-fifth Synod of the Evangelical Lutheran Ministerium of the State of New York, and the adjacent States and Countries, held at Churchtown, Columbia county, N. Y., August 31 to Sept. 3, 1850. 8°, pp. 35.

SELMSER, JOHN. Minutes of the Twentieth Annual Session of the Hartwick Synod of the Evangelical Lutheran Church in the State of New York. 8°, pp. 32.
> 500 copies.

SEYMOUR, DAVID L. Synopsis of Titles and Decisions of Questions of Quarter Sales, Taxes, Assessments, etc., on Van Rensselaer's Manor. 8°, pp. 50.

SIMMS, JEPTHA R. Trappers of New York, or a Biography of Nicholas Stoner and Nathaniel Foster ; together with Anecdotes of other Celebrated Hunters, and some Account of Sir William Johnson, and his Style of Living. 12°, pp. 287.
　　1,000 copies.　Plates.　Several editions of this have been printed.

SMITH, CHARLES ADAM. Illustrations of Faith, drawn from the Word of God. 18°, pp. 160.
　　500 copies.

SMITH, CHARLES ADAM. The Ground of National Consolation and Hope : a Sermon occasioned by the Death of Zachary Taylor, late President of the United States, delivered in the Third Lutheran Church of Rhinebeck, on Sabbath morning, July 21, 1850. 8°, pp. 30.

SMITH, THOMAS. Walker's Critical Pronouncing Dictionary and Expositor of the English Language abridged ; in which not only the meaning of every Word is explained, and the sound of every syllable distinctly shown, but where words are subject to different Pronunciations, the best Pronunciation is selected ; also, containing a Table of the Simple and Diphthongal Vowels referred to by the Figures over the Letters in this Dictionary. 16°, pp. 411.

STARR, J. LEANDER. Statement in behalf of the National Loan Fund Life Assurance Association of London, in regard to the Claim of Mrs. Hertzell. 8°, pp. 16.

STATEMENTS of the National Loan Fund L. A. Association. 8°, pp. 16.
　　300 copies.　Not on file.

STATEMENT relating to the Double Wharfage collected at the City of Albany, and explanatory of the Bill now before the Legislature. 8°, pp. 4.

STEVENSON, JAMES. Report of the Water Commissioners to the Hon. the Mayor and Common Council of the City of Albany, relative to supplying the City with Water ; Albany, Sept. 20, 1850. 8°, pp. 16.

STREET, OWEN. A Sermon on the Death of Mrs. Cornelia A. Lansingh, delivered in the Congregational Church at Jamestown, Chautauqua county, N. Y., on Thursday, Feb. 7, 1850. 8°, pp. 31.
　　500 copies.

THIRTY-NINTH Annual Report of the Albany County Bible Society. 12°, pp. 12.

THURMAN, JOHN R. Address of the Hon. John R. Thurman, Representative of the Fifteenth Congressional District of New York, to his constituents. 8°, pp. 7.
　　3,000 copies.

TILLINGHAST, JOHN L. [A pamphlet without title on the subject of wharfage in the Albany Basin, intended to be appended to another pamphlet on that subject.] 8°, pp. 17.

1851.

ANNUAL CATALOGUE of the Officers and Students of Hartwick Theological
and Classical Seminary, for the Academic year ending Aug. 27, 1851,
12°, pp. 8.

BARNES, WILLIAM. The Settlement, and Early History of Albany; a
Prize Essay, delivered before the Young Men's Association, Dec. 26,
1850. 8°, pp. 25.
    300 copies.

BARRINGTON, H. True Christian Union Required, and made Plain, by
the Words of the Third Angel, Rev. XIV, 9-11. 18°, pp. 52.
    1,200 copies. The Author was a monomaniac.

BAYLIES, FRANCIS. A Narrative of Major General Wool's Campaign in
Mexico, in the years 1846, 1847 and 1848. 8°, pp. 78.
    5,000 copies. Portrait.

BEARDSLEE, R. G. The Annual Report of the President of the Young
Men's Association for Mutual Improvement in the City of Albany,
made at its Eighteenth Annual Meeting, Feb. 5, 1851. 8°, pp. 38.
    400 copies.

BUCKHOUT, EDWARD A. The Dutch Almanac for 1851. 12°, pp. 24.
    5,000 copies.

BULLIONS, PETER. Principles of English Grammar; comprising the Substance of the most approved English Grammars extant; with copious
exercises in Parsing and Syntax; a new Edition, revised, rearranged
and improved, for the use of Schools. 12°, pp. xii, 224.

BY-LAWS of Independence Hook and Ladder Company No. 1, of the City
of Albany; revised and adopted May 1, 1841. 16°, pp. 8.

CADY. Opinion of Judge Cady, in Supreme Court, the People of the State
of New York vs. George Clarke: Hon. L. S. Chatfield, attorney general,
and John Van Buren, for plaintiffs; Hon. Samuel Beardsley, Nicholas
Hill, Jr., and Richard Cooper for defendants. Judgment for defendant,
George Clark. 8°, pp. 41.
    750 copies.

CATALOGUE and Circular of the Albany Medical College. 8°, pp. 24.
    3,000. Not on file.

CATALOGUE of Books in the Sabbath School Library of the First Presbyterian Church, Jan. 1, 1852. 16°, pp. 16.

CATALOGUE of the Conference Academy. 8°, pp. 24.
    1,000 copies.

CATALOGUE of the New York Conference Seminary. 8°, pp. 23.
    1,000 copies.

CATALOGUE of the Sabbath School Library connected with the Arbor
Hill M. E. church. 18°, pp. 8.
    500 copies.

CHARTER of the First Company of the Great Western Turnpike Road, granted by the Legislature of the State of New York, March 15, 1799. and April 5, 1802, together with all Acts amendatory thereof now in force. 12°, pp. 40.
50 copies.

CIRCULAR of the Law School of the University of Albany, for the year 1851-2. 8°, pp. 16.
3,500 copies.

CIRCULAR. To the Friends of Education in the State of New York. 8°, pp. 4.

CLARE, MARIA J. [Margaret Cook]. The Trial. 12°, pp. 70.
500 copies.

COLTON, AARON. Colton's improved Patent Bee-Hive, with Instructions for making and using, together with Directions for Managing Bees in the manner most profitable to their owners. 16°, pp. 16.

CONSTITUTION and By-Laws of the Albany Club; organized May 1, 1851. 18°, pp. 8.

CONSTITUTION and By-Laws of the Albany Republican Artillery. 16°, pp. 16.
300 copies.

CONSTITUTION and By-Laws of the Albany Scotch Light Infantry ; organized 1851. 18°, pp. 18.
150 copies.

CONSTITUTION and By-Laws of the Kinderhook Division, No. 164, of the Sons of Temperance, of the State of New York. 18°, pp. 35.

CONSTITUTION and Rules of the Albany Axe Company; adopted June 3, 1839. 18°, pp. 12.

CONSULTUS, Juris. Constitutional Law. [In relation to stay of proceedings in certain cases.] 8°, pp. 4.

COPY Articles of Agreement between the Buffalo and State Line Rail Road Company, the Dunkirk and State Line Rail Road, the New York and Erie Rail Road Company, and the Buffalo and Rochester Rail Road Company. 8°, pp. 7.

DAVY, J. [Margaret Skerritt.] Chemistry and Familar Science; containing, in a condensed form, the Elementary Principles, and all the most important Facts of the Science. 12°, pp. 295.
1,000 copies.

DEVOL, C. Multum in Parvo; Captivity of the Human Race; Revolution by Jesus Christ: The Protracted and Desperate Campaign ; Biographical Sketches of Scripture Characters; Three Hundred Scripture allusions and quotations, or Running History of Earth and Time; Retrospect of Earth and Time from beyond the Judgment. 8°, pp. 23.

Die Gott Loseste und nie gehörte Mordthat in den Annalen der Verbrechen: Leben und Bekenntniss des ueberfuehrten und hingerichteten Ruben A Dunbar: wegen der Emordung des Stephan A. und David L. Lester, (alter 8 und 10 Jahren) zu Westerlo, county Albany, am 28ten Sept. 1850. 8° pp. 26.
Portrait on wood.

Exercises of the Alumnæ of the Albany Female Academy, on their Tenth Anniversary, July, 1851. 8°, pp. 49.

Fifteenth Annual Report of the Albany City Tract Society, made at the Congregational Church, Dec. 15, 1850. 12°, pp. 13.
1,500 copies.

Fortieth Annual Report of the Albany County Bible Society. 12°, pp. 12.
1,000 copies.

Goodale, M. S. A Historical Discourse of the Presbyterian Church of Amsterdam Village; delivered July 6, 1851. 8°, pp. 22.
250 copies.

Hammond, Jabez D. Address delivered on the occasion of the Dedication of the New York Conference Academy, at Charlotteville, Schoharie Co., Nov. 8, 1850. 8°, pp. 20.
500 copies.

Hammond, Jabez D. On the Evidence independent of Written Revelation, of the Immortality of the Soul: an Address delivered before the Young Men's Association of the City of Albany, Feb. 28, 1850. 8°, pp. 23.
250 copies.

Hammond, S. S. The Closing Argument in the Case of the People vs. Reuben Dunbar, for Murder; tried at the late November Term of the Court of Oyer and Terminer for Albany County. 8°, pp. 32.
1,000 copies.

Harsha, D. A. Thoughts on the Love of Christ, as Manifested to a Lost World. 18°, pp. 192.
1,000 copies.

Haven, C. W. The Manhattan Souvenir, and New York Sketch Book, for 1851. 12°, pp. 96.

Holden, A. W. Early Voyages of Discovery — First attempts to establish a Colony in Canada — Discovery of Northern New York, by Samuel de Champlain, in 1609 — Battle between the Algonquins and Iroquois. 8°, pp. 8.
Intended as a sample of a History of Warren County, New York.

Holmes, Edwin. Minutes of the Particular Synod of Albany, convened at Albany, May 7, 1851. 8°, pp. 33.
200 copies.

Howard, Nathan, Jr. Practice Reports in the Supreme Court and Court of Appeals of the State of New York. Vol. V, 8°, vii, 503.

Kennedy, Duncan. A Discourse delivered Oct. 1, 1851, on occasion of the Inauguration of the Rev. William H. Campbell, D. D., as Professor

of Biblical Literature, in the Theological Seminary of the Reformed
Dutch Church, New Brunswick, N. J.   8°, pp. 48.
500 copies.

LANE, SAURIN ELLIOT.   Temperance, a Christian Duty; Abstinence, a
Matter of Christian Liberty.   8°, pp. 34.
500 copies.

LAYMAN.   [John Fine.]   Lecture on the Resurrection of the Body; compiled from the Writings of Paul, Dick, Hall and others.   8°, pp. 24.
100 copies. John Fine died, Jan., 1867. He was for many years an available subject for a lay delegate to Presbyterian Synods, where being of a goodly presence he
maintained an enviable dignity. Hence he may have caught the ambition of shining
as a writer of lay sermons. His chirography was a terror to type setters.

LELAND, CHARLES P.   Capt. Leland's Report of the Horrible Sacrifices of
Human Victims among the Wild Tribes of India, and also of the Self-
Sacrifices so prevalent in that country.   8°, pp. 36.

LETTERS Patent to W. Woodworth.   [For Planing Machines.]   8°, pp. 16.
500 copies.

McDONALD, W. H.   Advertising, its Advantages to Business, how, when,
and where to do it.   12°, pp. 16.
500 copies.

MILES, JOHN.   Review of Bishop Hughes's Sermon on the Decline of Pro-
testantism ; a Lecture, delivered in the Albany Bethel, Sabbath Evening,
Dec. 15, 1850.   8°, pp. 16.
2,000 copies.

MINUTES of the Fifty-fifth Anniversary of the Rensselaerville Baptist
Association, held with the Baptist Church in Preston Hollow, Sept. 17,
1851.   12°, pp. 16.
600 copies.

MINUTES of the Twenty-first Annual Session of the Hartwick Synod.
8°, pp. 26.
500 copies. Not on file.

MITCHELL, THOMAS.   The Gospel Crown of Life ; a System of Philosophical Theology.   12°, pp. xvii, 417.
1,000 copies.

MUNSELL, HEZ.   Manual of Practical English Grammar, on a new and
easy Plan ; for Schools, Families and Self-Instruction.   12°, pp. 66.
500 copies.

MUNSELL, JOEL.   Hoffman & Munsell's Albany Directory and City Register, for 1851-52, with a Map and Index.   12°, pp. 460.
1,000 copies.

MUNSELL, JOEL.   Webster's Calendar, or the Albany Almanac for the
year of our Lord 1852.   12°, pp. 36.

PAINE, HENRY D.   Proceedings of the Homœopathic Medical Society of
the State of New York.   8°, pp. 12.
500 copies.

PALMER, RAY.   Christ going forth to Purify the World ; a Sermon
preached before the Foreign Evangelical Society, New York, May 7,
1848.   8°, pp. 34.
500 copies.

PALMER, RAY. Closet Hours; or Aids to Spiritual Improvement, and
Practical Religion. 12°, pp. 311.
1,000 copies.

PARKER, AMASA J. An Address delivered before the Graduating Class of
the Albany Medical College, January 21, 1851. 8°, pp. 32.
400 copies.

PARMENTER and VAN ANTWERP. Directory of the City of Hudson, for
the year 1851-52. 18°, pp. 70.
500 copies.

PEASE, ERASTUS H. Semi-Monthly Advertiser. 8°, pp. 28.
5,350 copies.

PEASE, FREDERICK S. A Family Gathering. 8°, pp. 4.

PROGRAMME of the Exercises at the Dedication of the New Rooms of the
Young Men's Association. Dec. 10, 1851. 8°, pp. 4.

RATHBONE & Co., Stove Manufacturers, Office Nos. 9 and 11 Green Street ;
Foundry North Ferry Street. 8°, pp. 28.
500 copies. Circular.

[RAWSON, T. R.] City Missionary Society, Abstract from the Eighth
Annual Report, presented May 3, 1851. 12°, pp. 16.
500 copies.

REPORT of the District Grand Committee of the District of Albany, relative to District Grand Committees. 8°, pp. 12.

RULES and Regulations for the Government of the Evangelical Lutheran
Ebenezer Church, in the City of Albany; adopted Feb., 1851. 12°,
pp. 11.

[SCHOLL, WILLIAM N.] Minutes of the Fifty-sixth Session of the Evangelical Lutheran Ministerium of the State of New York, and adjacent States
and Countries, held at Saddle-River, Bergen Co., N. J., September 6
to 9, 1851. 8°, pp. 34.
500 copies.

SELKIRK, EDWARD. To the Parishioners of Trinity Church. 8°, pp. 3.

SMITH, EGBERT T. Speech of the Hon. Egbert T. Smith, of Suffolk, in
the Assembly of New York, upon the Union Resolutions, Feb. 17,
1851. 8°, pp. 8.

SPENCER, JOHN C. By-Laws, Rules and Regulations of the Albany
Hospital ; and a list of the Governors and Officers; with the Act of Incorporation. 8°, pp. 33.
250 copies.

SPENCER, JOHN C. Review of the Testimony given before the General
Court Martial, upon the Trial of Brig. General George Talcott, in June
and July, 1851; and of the Proceedings of the Court, to which is
appended a copy of the Record of the Trial. By a Counsellor at
Law. 8°, pp. 46, 112.
1,000 copies.

SUMMARY of Faith and Rules of Discipline of the Ev. Lutheran Church
of Lockport, N. Y. 18°, pp. 8.
500 copies.

TATOR, HENRY H. An Oration Commemorative of the Birthday of Washington, delivered in the Methodist Episcopal Church at Francisville, Schoharie county, N. Y., on the 22d of February, 1851. 8°, pp. 21.
200 copies.

TATOR, HENRY H. An Oration Commemorative of the Character of Alexander Hamilton. 8°, pp. 22.
200 copies.

TATOR, HENRY H. An Oration Commemorative of the Character of Mrs. Mary Washington. 8°, pp. 20.
200 copies.

THIRD Annual Report of the Inspectors of the Albany County Penitentiary. with the Documents accompanying the same, made to the Board of Supervisors of the County of Albany, and the mayor and recorder of the city of Albany, in Joint Meeting assembled, on the 2d day of December, 1851. 8°, pp. 44.
1,200 copies.

THOMPSON, MARGARET. Phrenological Character of Reuben Dunbar, with a short Treatise on the Causes and Prevention of Crime. 8°, pp. 16.
3,000 copies. Portrait on wood.

TWENTIETH Annual Report of Directors of the Albany Orphan Asylum, Jan., 1851. 12°, pp. 12.
500 copies.

VANDERBURGH, F. Similia Similibus Curantur: Annual Address delivered in Albany, before the Academy of Medicine of the State of New York, February 19th, 1851. 8°, pp. 29.

WALKER, AARON G. The Life of Jerringham Cauffman, a great American Resurrectionist, or Robber of the Grave; containing thrilling Accounts of Depredations upon the Grave, committed in different sections of the Country; particularly in the Vicinities of our large Cities and Towns, such as Philadelphia, Boston, Baltimore, New York, Cincinnati, Portland, Pittsburgh, Providence, Albany, Buffalo, &c.; also, an Account of his Deathbed, and Confession of the foregoing. 8°, pp. 63.
4,000 copies. Cuts.

WHEELER, MELICK & Co. Catalogue of Machines and Implements manufactured and sold by the Proprietors at their Works, corner of Hamilton and Liberty Streets, Albany, N. Y., near the Steam Boat Landing, and by their agents throughout the Union. 12°, pp. 12.

1852.

ALBANY and Rensselaer Horticultural Society: List of Officers and Committees, Constitution, Rules and Regulations, and List of Premiums for 1852. 8°, pp. 16.
200 copies.

ANNUAL Catalogue of the Officers and Students of Hartwick Theological and Classical Seminary, for the Academic year ending Aug. 25, 1852. 8°, pp. 8.
250 copies.

APPEAL of Hugh A. Mosier to the Quarterly Conference of the Methodist Episcopal Church. 8°, pp. 17.
And table.

BANK Book of Albany City Savings Institution. 12°, pp. 16.

BECKER, ABRAHAM. Address before the Faculty and Students of the New York Conference Seminary, and Citizens of Charlotteville, N. Y., July 5, 1852, at their Celebration of the 77th Anniversary of American Independence. 8°, pp. 16.
500 copies.

BECKER, ABRAHAM, and ROBERT F. QUEAL. Address delivered at Worcester, N. Y., July 26, 1852, on the occasion of the Burial of Capt. Leslie Chase, of the United States Army, and Poem delivered on the same occasion. 8°, pp. 23.
600 copies.

BEMENT, CALEB N. Catalogue of Articles manufactured and prepared at the City Steam Mills, by C. N. Bement, No 341 Broadway, Albany; to which is added Hints from Cousin Susan's Receipt Book, containing Eighty-Five Receipts for Making Bread, Cakes, Pies, Puddings, Blanc-Mange, Soups, etc., etc. 18°, pp. 36.
1,000 copies.

BOWEN, T. H. Rules for Punctuation. 12°, pp. 8.

BUCKHOUT, EDWARD A. The Dutch Almanac for 1852. 12°, pp. 24.
5,000 copies.

BY-LAWS of Chatham Lodge, I. O. of O. F., 18°, pp. 24.
250 copies. Not on file.

BY-LAWS of Forest Tent, No 175. 12°, pp. 24.
500 copies. Not on file.

BY-LAWS of Iris Lodge No 359, I. O. of O. F., Coeymans, N. Y. 12°, pp. 8.

CARRIER's Address to the Patrons of the Albany Daily State Register. 8°, pp. 4.
400 copies.

CASES and Points in the Supreme Court of the State of New York. 8°.

CATALOGUE and Circular of the Albany Medical College. 8°, pp. 16.
7,000 copies. Not on file.

CATALOGUE and Circular of the Law School of the University of Albany for the year 1852. 8°.
2,500 copies. Not on file.

CATALOGUE of Books in the Sabbath School Library of the First Presbyterian Church, Jan. 1, 1852. 16°, pp. 16.

CATALOGUE of Books in the Sabbath School Library of the Pearl street Baptist Church. 18°, pp. 24.

CATALOGUE of the Albany Academy. 8°, pp. 32.
1,000 copies. Not on file.

CATALOGUE of the Delta Kappa Fraternity, Yale and Amherst. 12°, pp. 18.
300 copies.

CATALOGUE of the Lyceum of Natural History of Williams College, instituted A. D. 1835. 8°, pp. 60.
500 copies.

CATALOGUE of the Officers and Students of Great Barrington Academy, for the Academic year 1851–2. 8°, pp. 12.
450 copies. Plate.

CATALOGUE of the Sunday School Library of the Hudson Street Methodist Episcopal Church, Albany, Jan. 15, 1852. 18°, pp. 25.
300 copies.

CHARTER of the Village of Greenbush, with all the Amendments. 8°, pp. 11.

CIRCULAR and Catalogue of Mrs. Brinckerhoff's Boarding and Day School for Young Ladies, No 112 State street, Albany. 12°, pp. 8.

CIRCULAR and Catalogue of the New York Conference Seminary. 8°, pp. 24.
1,800 copies. There seems to have been three editions. Not on file.

COLORED Home of the City of New York. 12°, pp. 8.

CONSTITUTION and By-Laws of Beacon Light Division, No. 536, of the Sons of Temperance of Schenectady county, N. Y.; instituted June 30, 1849. 18°, pp. 27.
250 copies.

CONSTITUTION and By-Laws of Enrogel Lodge, No. 406, I. O. O. F. 18°, pp. 34.

CONSTITUTION and By-Laws of the Sunday School Association, of the Albany West Station M. E. Church, adopted Jan., 1852. 12°, pp. 13.
200 copies.

CONSTITUTION and By-Laws of the Sunday School Association of the Albany West Station M. E. Church, adopted Jan., 1852. 16°, pp. 16.

CONSTITUTION, By-Laws, and Rules of Order of New York Encampment of Patriarchs No. 1, of Northern New York. 18°, pp. 36.
200 copies.

CONSTITUTION of Friendly Union Lodge, No. 91.
200 copies. Not on file.

COPY of Articles of Agreement; Great Western Rail Road Company, Canada West. 8°, pp. 9.

DAVENPORT, JAMES R. The Lord our Helper; a Sermon in Commemoration of the Sixth Anniversary of the Commencement of the Parish of Grace Church, Albany, preached on Sexagesima Sunday, Feb. 15, 1852. 12°, pp. 22.

[DEDERICK, REUBEN.] Minutes of the Twenty-Second Annual Session of the Hartwick Synod, of the Evangelical Lutheran Church, in the State of New York.
500 copies.

EXERCISES of the Alumnæ of the Albany Female Academy on their Eleventh Anniversary, June, 1852. 8°, pp. 92.
350 copies. Not on file.

FIRE Limit Law, City of Albany, passed Oct. 11, 1855. 8°, pp. 3.

[FORSYTH, WILLIAM W.] Third Annual Report of the Inspectors of the Albany County Penitentiary, with the Documents accompanying the same, made to the Board of Supervisors of the county of Albany, and the Mayor and Recorder of the City of Albany, in Joint Meeting assembled, on the second day of December, 1851. 8°, 44.
> Steel plate.

FORTY-FIRST Annual Report of the Albany County Bible Society. 12°, pp. 12.

HARSHA, DAVID A. Christ and Him Crucified; the Sum and Substance of the Gospel, the only Hope of the Sinner, and the Glory of the Christian. 18°, pp. 195.
> 500 copies.

HARSHA, DAVID A. Immanuel's Land; or a Glimpse of the World of Glory. 32°, pp. 123.
> 600 copies.

HARSHA, DAVID A. The Principles of Hydropathy, or the Invalid's Guide to Health and Happiness; being a plain familiar Exposition of the Principles of the Water Cure System. 12°, pp. 52.
> 500 copies.

HAWLEY, GIDEON. Essay on Knowledge. 8°, pp. 131.
> 25 copies. This was privately printed, in several editions, each much changed, after having been submitted to learned men to get opinions and suggestions.

HOWARD, NATHAN, Jr. Practice Reports in the Supreme Court and Court of Appeals of the State of New York. Vol. VI, 8°, pp. iv, 531.

HUNTINGTON, EZRA A. The Strife for Supremacy in the Church : a Sermon preached at the opening of the Synod of Albany, in the First Presbyterian Church, Albany, Oct. 12, 1852. 8°, pp. 36.
> 300 copies.

JOHNSTON, JAMES F. W. Catechism of Agricultural Chemistry and Geology; with an Introduction by John Pitkin Norton. 16°, pp. 80.
> 1,000 copies.

JOHNSON, JAMES J. The Annual Report of the President and Standing Committees of the Young Men's Association for Mutual Improvement, in the City of Albany, made at its 19th Annual Meeting, Feb. 4, 1852. 8°, pp. 52.
> 400 copies.

KIP, WILLIAM INGRAHAM. The Kindred Dead. 8°, pp. 21.

LAST Will and Testament of John L. Sill. 8°, pp. 8.

LAST Will and Testament of William Barthrop, deceased, of Kinderhook, N. Y. 8°, pp. 15.

LINTNER, G. A. A Memoir of the Rev. Walter Gunn, late Missionary in India, from the Evangelical Lutheran Church in the United States. 18° pp. 156.
> 1,000 copies.

LIST of Officers and Members of Hope Lodge, No. 1, I. O. of O. F., Albany, April 1, 1852. 18°, pp. 6.
150 copies.

MANOR of Rensselaerwyck; Supreme Court, Rensselaer County. Opinion of Judge Harris in the Case of the People vs. William P. Van Rensselaer and others. 8°, pp. 8.

MANUAL of the First Presbyterian Church of Hudson. 18°, pp. 16.
700 copies.

MANVIL, MRS. Lucinda,, or the Mountain Mourner; being Authentic Facts in a series of Letters. 12°, pp. 168.
1,000 copies.

MILLS, B. F. & J. A. Catalogue of a Select School for Boys. 12°, pp. 12.
300 copies. Not on file.

MINUTES of the Fifty-seventh Session of the Evangelical Lutheran Ministerium of the State of New York, and adjacent States and Countries, held at Red Hook, Dutchess Co., N. Y., Aug. 23 to Sept. 1, 1852. 8°, pp. 44.
500 copies.

MINUTES of the Fifty-sixth Anniversary of the Rensselaerville Baptist Association, held with the Baptist Church in Duanesburgh, Schenectady County, N. Y., Sept. 15th and 16th, 1852. 12°, pp. 24.

MULTER, JACOB J. The Farmer's Law Book and Town Officer's Guide: containing the Election, Qualifications and Duties of the Supervisor, Justice of the Peace, Constable, Collector, Town Clerk, Assessors, Overseer of the Poor, Commissioners and Overseers of Highways, Pound-Master, Town Sealer, Common School Officers, and Executors and Administrators; and the Laws concerning Apprenticeship, Arbitration, Bailment, Bills of Exchange and Promissory Notes, Bonds, Contracts, and Agreements, Deeds, Descent of Real and Personal Property, Fences, Fire, Fraud and Deceit, Husband and Wife, Infancy, Landlord and Tenant, Malicious, and other Animals, Mortgages, Nuisance, Parent and Child, Partnership, Principal and Agent, Roads, Rules of Evidence, Slander, Statute of Limitations, Strays, Tender, Trespass, Trover, Usury, Warranty, Water and Watercourses, Wills, etc., etc., with Legal Forms, under each general division of Process; Pleadings and Proceedings in Justice's Courts; and also of Bonds, Bills, Notes, Deeds, Mortgages, Real and Personal, Articles of Copartnership, Assignments, Leases, Releases, Submissions, Awards, Orders, Notices, &c., &c., with a copious Index. Second Edition. 12°, pp. 394.
2,000 copies.

MUNSELL, J. The Annals of Albany. Vol. III. 12°, pp. 380.
500 copies.

MUNSELL, J. Webster's Calendar, or the Albany Almanac for the year of our Lord 1853. 12°, pp. 36.
30,000 copies.

NEW YORK Conference Seminary; Gentlemen and Ladies Exhibition; Tuesday and Wednesday, Oct. 28 and 29, 1852. 12°, pp. 4.

NINTH Annual Report of the Albany City Missionary Society, presented May, 1852. 12°, pp. 12.
500 copies.

PAINE, HENRY D. An Address to the Homœopathic Physicians of the State of New York, together with the Constitution and By-Laws of the Homœopathic Medical Society of the State of New York. 8°.

PALMER, RAY. Address on the Education of Woman, delivered at the Anniversary of the Pittsfield Young Ladie's Institute, September 30, 1852. 8°, pp. 31.
1,000 copies.

PRUYN, SAMUEL. First Annual Report of the Inspectors of the Albany County Penitentiary, with the Reports of the Superintendent, Physician and Chaplain, made to the Board of Supervisors of the County of Albany and the Mayor and Recorder of the City of Albany, in Joint Meeting Assembled, December 27th, 1849. Including an Account of the Origin and History of the Penitentiary, the Rules and Regulations established for its Government, a Description of the Buildings, accompanied by Plans and Diagrams thereof, and other matter connected with the enterprise. Compiled, at the request of the Authorities, by the Commissioners for building the Penitentiary, from the Reports made by them at various times during the progress of the work. 8°, pp. 80.
1,500 copies. Mr. Pruyn never found time to finish this report, which was intended to embrace a history of the origin and progress of the institution from its inception to its occupation. It was not issued till after the third annual report, when only 100 copies went out as far as printed, and the remainder was finally sold for waste paper, after Mr. Pruyn's death.

RATHBONE & Co. Circular for 1852. 8°, pp. 36.
500 copies.

RAWLINGS, AUGUSTUS. Eulogy on Daniel Webster. 8°, pp. 25.
300 copies. Not on file.

REAGLES, C. & SON. Catalogue of Fruit and Ornamental Trees, cultivated at the Union Nurseries, No 12 Barrett Street, Schenectady, N. Y. 12°, pp. 12.
400 copies.

ROSSEEL, JOSEPH A. Funeral Discourse on the death of Allison Remington Bowen, delivered in the Presbyterian Church, Evans's Mills, Jefferson County, N. Y., March 22, 1852. 8°, pp. 23.
250 copies.

SCHERMERHORN, J. W. Essay before the Literary Societies of the State Normal School, Jan. 31, 1852. 8°, pp. 9.

SECOND Annual Report of the Troy Conference Missionary Society, auxiliary to the Missionary Society of the Methodist Episcopal Church, 1852. 12°, pp. 36.
5,000 copies.

SIXTEENTH Annual Report of the Albany City Tract Society, made at the First Presbyterian Church, December 21, 1851. 12°, pp. 16.
1,500 copies.

SMITH, CHARLES ADAM. A Discourse delivered on the occasion of the Birth of Washington, before the National Guards of Easton, Pa., in Christ Church, Sabbath morning, Feb, 22, 1852. 8°, pp. 26.
500 copies.

SMITH, CHARLES A. Fourth July Sermon. 8°, pp. 23.
200 copies. Not on file.

SPENCER, JOHN C. Proceedings at the Opening of the Albany Hospital, November 1, 1851; with a List of the Contributors, and of the Officers of the Institution, and Information respecting the Admission of Patients. 8°, pp. 15.
500 copies.

STREET, ALFRED B. A Poem delivered at the Anniversary of the Pittsfield Young Ladies' Institute, Sept. 30, 1852. 8°, pp. 8.
1,000 copies.

SWEET, SAMUEL NILES. Practical Elocution: containing illustrations of the Principles of Reading and Public Speaking, also a selection of the best Pieces from Ancient and Modern Authors, accompanied by Explanatory Notes; the whole adapted to the purposes of Improvement in Reading and Oratory. 12°, pp. 312.
1,000 copies.

TATOR, HENRY H. An Eulogy Commemorative of the Character of Hon. Henry Clay. 8°, pp. 22.
200 copies.

TATOR, HENRY H. An Oration Commemorative of the Character of Patrick Henry. 8°, pp. 24.
200 copies.

TATOR, HENRY H. An Oration Commemorative of the Character of Thomas Jefferson. 8°, pp. 22.
250 copies.

TRACT for Otis Allen. pp. 12.
800 copies. Not on file.

VALENTINE, T. W. The New York Teacher, a Monthly Periodical, devoted to the Cause of General Education, but designed particularly as the Organ of the Teachers' Association of the State of New York. Vol. I. 8°, pp. 392.
1,200 copies.

WALL, EDWARD. The Psalmist's Exhortation to his Soul. A Discourse delivered on Thursday, Nov. 25, 1852, the day of Annual Thanksgiving in New York, in the Congregational Church in Kingsborough, N. Y. 8°, pp. 14.
300 copies.

[WELLS, JUSTIN.] Narrative of the Reflections of Justin Wells, compiled from Manuscripts written by Himself. 18°, pp. 96.
1,000 copies from his plates.

WYCKOFF, ISAAC N. Anna the Prophetess: a Funeral Sermon, occasioned by the Death of Mrs. Anna Lansing, widow of Jacob J. Lansing, delivered in the Middle Dutch Church, June 13, 1852. 8°, pp. 24.
100 copies.

WYCKOFF, ISAAC N. The Stability of the Times: a Sermon delivered on the Fourth of July, 1852, in the Second Reformed Protestant Dutch Church, in the City of Albany. 8°, pp. 34.
500 copies.

YALE, ELISHA. Eldership in the Church of God, inscribed to the Congregational Church in Kingston, N. Y. 12°, pp. 15.
500 copies.

1853.

AGREEMENT between the Albany and Schenectady Rail Road Company, the Schenectady and Troy Rail Road Company, the Utica and Schenectady Rail Road Company, the Mohawk Valley Rail Road Company, the Syracuse and Utica Rail Road Company, the Rochester and Syracuse Rail Road Company, the Buffalo and Rochester Rail Road Company, the Rochester and Niagara Falls Rail Road Company. and the Buffalo and Lockport Rail Road Company; whereby the said Companies are consolidated into one Corporation, under the Name of the New York Central Rail Road Company, in pursuance of an act of the Legislature of the State of New York, entitled " An Act to authorize. the Consolidation of Certain Rail Road Companies, passed April 2d, 1853. 8°, pp. 36.
580 copies.

ANNUAL Catalogue of the Officers and Students of Hartwick Theological and Classical Seminary, for the Academic year ending May 24, 1853, 8°, pp. 12.

ANNUAL Circular of Emery & Company, Proprietors of the Albany Agricultural Works, Corner of Hamilton, Liberty and Union Streets, Warehouse and Seed Store 369, 371 and 373 Broadway, Albany, N. Y. 8°, pp. 8.
8,000 copies.

ARTICLES of Association of the Merchants' Bank of Albany. 12°, pp. 10.
500 copies.

ARTICLES of Faith and Covenant, together with the Principles of Government and Discipline, adopted by the First Congregational Church, Albany. 12°, pp. 16.

BURGESS, GEORGE. The Gospel in its first Progress Westward. A Sermon preached in Trinity Church, New York, on Friday, Oct. 28, 1853, (the Festival of St. Simon and St. Jude), at the Consecration of the Rev. W. Ingraham Kip, D. D., as Missionary Bishop of California. 8°, pp. 25.
500 copies.

BY-LAWS of the Albany and Susquehanna Rail Road Company. 8°, pp. 11.
250 copies.

BY-LAWS of the New York State Medical Society. 8°, pp. 42.
500 copies.

CATALOGUE and Circular of the Albany Medical College, Fall Term, 1854. 8°, pp. 16.
7,000 copies.

CATALOGUE and Circular of the Law School of the University of Albany, for the year 1853–4. 8°, pp. 16.
3,000 copies.

CATALOGUE of Richmondville Union Seminary. 8°, pp. 42.
2,000 copies.

CATALOGUE of the Officers and Pupils of the Unadilla Academy, for the Academic year, 1852–3. 8°, pp. 16.
200 copies.

CATALOGUE of the Trustees, Instructors and Pupils of the Albany Female Seminary, for the year 1852–3 ; with the Reports of the Examining Committees for 1853. 8°, pp. 21.
500 copies. Plate.

CATTLE Keeper's Guide, and Every Man his own Doctor. 12°, pp. 44.
500 copies.

CHARTER of the Young Men's Association for Mutual Improvement in the City of Albany: together with the Rules and Regulations adopted and revised by the Executive Committee for the Government of the Association in the Several Departments, Dec., 1852. 8°, pp. 23.

CONSTITUTION and By-Laws of Bash-au-Bish Lodge No. 434, I. O. O. F. of the State of New York ; instituted at Copake, May 10, 1853. 18°, pp. 45.
150 copies.

CONSTITUTION and By-Laws of Richmondville Lodge No. 446, Independent Order of Odd-Fellows of Northern New York, organized Jan. 27, 1853. 18°, pp. 35.
500 copies.

CONSTITUTION and By-Laws of the Church Brotherhood of Albany. 18°, pp. 24.
300 copies.

CONSTITUTION and Rules of the Albany Axe Company; adopted June 1, 1839. 18°, pp. 9.
125 copies.

CONSTITUTION, By-Laws and Rules of Morning Star Lodge, No. 128, I. O. of O. F. of the State of New York. Instituted at Chatham Four Corners, Oct. 7, 1844. 18°, pp. 38.
500 copies.

EXERCISES of the Alumnæ of the Albany Female Academy, on their Twelfth Anniversary, June 22d, 1853. 8°, pp. 45.
400 copies.

FORTY-SECOND Annual Report of the Albany County Bible Society. 12° pp. 12.

GENEALOGY of the Ancestry and Posterity of Isaac Lawrence, and Centennial Meeting of his Descendants, Nov. 27, 1851. 8°, pp. 76.

GENEALOGY of the Bissell Family. 8°, pp. 16.

GENEALOGY of the Hayden Family. 8°, pp. 15.

GENEALOGY of the Stiles Family. 8°, pp. 31.

GENEALOGY of the Windsor Family of Munsell. 8vo, pp. 8.

GOOCH, JOHN. Catalogue of Books, and Supplement. 8°, pp. 15, 10.
600 copies.

HARSHA, JNO. W. The Nature, Effects, and Pardon of Sin; to which is added a Warning and Exhortation to Sinners. 18°, pp. 241.
1,000 copies.

HOLCROFT, THOMAS. The Life of Baron Frederick Trenck; containing his Adventures, and also his excessive Sufferings during ten years' Imprisonment at the Fortress of Magdeburg, by command of Frederick the Great, King of Prussia. 8°, pp. 100.
1,000 copies. Printed for R. Spencer Dyer, superannuated printer.

HOLGATE, JEROME B. Conversations on the Present Age of the World, in Connection with Prophecy. 12°, pp. 332.
1,000 copies.

HOUGH, FRANKLIN B. A History of St. Lawrence and Franklin Counties, New York, from the Earliest Period to the Present Time. 8°, pp. xv. 719.
1,500. Portraits, maps, and wood cuts.

HOWARD, NATHAN, Jr. Practice Reports in the Supreme Court and Court of Appeals of the State of New York. Vol. VII, 8°, pp. v, 551.

JOHNSON, WILLIAM. Reports of Cases Argued and Determined, in the Supreme Court of Judicature, and in the Trial of Impeachment and the Correction of Errors, in the State of New York. 8°, pp. 399.
275 copies.

JOSLIN, B. F. Discovery of Curatives by Observation. An Address delivered in the Assembly Chamber, Albany, before the Homœopathic Medical Society of the State of New York, at its Annual Meeting, Feb. 8, 1853. 8°, pp. 24.
300 copies.

JOURNAL of the Sixteenth Annual Session of the Franckean Evangelic Lutheran Synod, convened at Fordsborough, Montgomery Co., N. Y., June 2, 1853. 8°, pp. 26.
500 copies.

McCALL, H. S. New Year's Address of the Carrier of the Albany Morning Express to its Patrons, Jan. 1, 1853. 12°, pp. 4.

MEMBERS of the National Congregational Convention, held October 5, 6, 7, 1852. 8°, pp. 5.
500 copies.

MEMORIAL in behalf of a County Map. 8°, pp. 8.

MEMORIALS of John Pitkin Norton, late Professor of Analytical and Agricultural Chemistry in Yale College, New Haven, Conn. 8°, pp. 85.
250 copies. Portrait.

MINUTES of the 50th Annual Synod, Albany. 8°, pp. 29.
2,000 copies.

MINUTES of the Fifty-eighth Session of the Evangelical Lutheran Ministerium of the State of New York, and adjacent States and Countries, held at Rhinebeck, Dutchess Co., N. Y., Sept. 6, 1853. 8°, pp. 37.
500 copies.

MINUTES of the Fifty-seventh Anniversary of the Rensselaerville Baptist Association held with the Baptist Church in Westerlo, Albany Co., N. Y., Sept. 21st and 22d, 1853. 12°, pp. 22.
700 copies.

MINUTES of the Particular Synod of Albany, convened at Albany, N. Y., May 5, 1853. 8°, pp. 33.
200 copies.

MINUTES of the Twenty-third Annual Session of the Hartwick Synod of the Evangelical Lutheran Church of the State of New York, convened at West Sandlake, Rensselaer Co., N. Y., Sept. 10, 1853. 8°, pp. 52.
500 copies.

MONTGOMERY, THOMAS. Literary Societies, their uses and abuses: an Address delivered before the Wesleyan Literary Association of the New York Conference Seminary, Charlotteville, Schoharie County, N. Y., Sept. 28, 1852. 8°, pp. 32.
500 copies.

MUNSELL, JOEL. Directory to the Trades in Albany, for the year 1853. 12°, pp. 62.
750 copies.

MUNSELL, JOEL. Munsell's Albany Directory and City Register for 1853–54. 12°, pp. 504.
1,200 copies.

MUNSELL, JOEL. The Annals of Albany. Vol. IV. 12°, pp. 405.
500 copies.

MUNSELL, JOEL. Webster's Calendar, or the Albany Almanac for the year of our Lord 1854. 12°, pp. 36.
30,000 copies.

PATTERN Lists. Smith & Co., Britannia and Silver Plated Ware. 1856, 4°, pp. 14. Rathbone & Kennedy, Stoves, 1856. 4°, pp. 16 — do. 1857, fol., pp. 41 — do. 1859, pp. 56. Vose & Co., 1853. fol., pp. 28. McCoy & Clark, 1860, 4 to, pp. 28.
Bound in one volume.

PEASE, A. G. Christ the Resurrection and the Life; a Sermon preached at the Funeral of Harry S. Richards, Esq., in the Congregational Church in Norwich, Vt., Wednesday, Nov. 6, 185). 8°, pp. 33.
250 copies.

PEASE, FREDERICK S. Genealogy of Isaac Lawrence. 8°, pp. 76.
200 copies.

PETER PUZZLEWIG'S Mirthful Game of Happy Hits at Useful Knowledge of Every Day Things. 24°, pp. 8.

PROCEEDINGS of the Forty-first Anniversary of the Washington County Bible Society, and anniversaries of other Benevolent Associations, held at Argyle, N. Y., Aug. 31 and Sept. 1, 1853. 12°, pp. 44.
1,000 copies.

PROCEEDINGS of the Forty-second Anniversary of the Washington County Bible Society, and other anniversaries of Benevolent Associations, held at Salem, N. Y. 12°, pp. 26.

PROCEEDINGS of the Homœopathic Medical Society of the State of New York. 1852–53. 8°, pp. 57.
1,500 copies.

RATHBONE & Co., Stove Manufacturers, Office No's 9 and 11 Green Street, Foundery North Ferry Street, Albany, N. Y. 8°, pp. 36.

REYNOLDS, DEXTER. A Treatise on the Law of Life Assurance. 8°, pp. 202.
1,500 copies.

RIVES, WILLIAM C. Connection of Agriculture with Free Political Institutions; comparative Position of Agriculture in Europe and America; Standard of Agricultural Profits in both Countries: an Address delivered at the Annual Exhibition of the New York State Agricultural Society, at Saratoga Springs, Sept. 23, 1853. 8°, pp. 28.

SEVENTEENTH Annual Report of the Albany City Tract Society, presented at the Middle Dutch Reformed Church, Dec. 19, 1852. 8°, pp. 24.
1,000 copies.

SIXTH Annual Report of the New York State Temperance Society, with the Proceedings of the Anniversary held in Rochester, June 16–17, 1853. 8°, pp. 40.
5,000 copies.

STONE, ROLLIN S. Manual for the Use of the Members of the Congregational Church in Danbury, Conn. 16°, pp. 24.
400 copies.

TENTH Annual Report of the Albany City Missionary Society, presented May, 1853. 12°, pp. 12.
500 copies.

TOWNSEND, FRANKLIN. List of Patterns formerly belonging to the Albany Eagle Foundry, and now the Property of Messrs. F. & T. Townsend, proprietors of Townsends' Furnace, Elk Street, Albany. Cap 8°, pp. 88.

TOWNSEND, HOWARD. The Introductory Lecture delivered before the Students of the Albany Medical College, Sept. 6, 1853. 8°, pp. 18.
350 copies.

TOWNSEND, THEODORE. The Annual Report of the President and Standing Committees of the Young Men's Association for Mutual Improvement in the City of Albany made at its twentieth Annual Meeting, Feb. 24, 1853. 8°, pp. 29.
400 copies.

TRIENNIAL Report of the Executive Committee of the Foreign Missionary Society of the Evangelical Lutheran Church in the United States, presented at Winchester, Va., May, 1853. 8°, pp. 24.

TWENTY-SECOND Anniversary of the Stephentown Baptist Association, held in the Meeting house of the Baptist Church at Lebanon Springs, Sept. 14, and 15, 1853. 8°, pp. 15.
400 copies.

1854.

ACCOUNT of the Ceremonies at the Laying of the Corner Stone of the New York Asylum for Idiots, at Syracuse, Sept. 8, 1854. 8°, pp. 44.
1,000 copies. Plates.

ALBANY Morning Express. Folio.
Daily Newspaper.

ANNUAL Catalogue of the Officers and Students of Hartwick Theological and Classical Seminary, for the Academic year ending August 23, 1854. 8°, pp. 12.
250 copies.

ANNUAL Circular of the Albany Agricultural Works, Warehouse and Seed Store. 8°, pp. 36.

ANNUAL Reports of the Albany Guardian Society and Home for the Friendless, for the years 1851, 1852, 1853. 12°, pp. 23.

ARTICLES of Association and By-Laws of the Guilderland Mutual Insurance Association. 12°, pp. 17.
500 copies.

BALL, ALONZO S. The Present Position of the Two Schools of Medicine; an Address delivered in the Assembly Chamber, Albany, before the Homœopathic Medical Society of the State of New York, at its Annual Meeting, February 14, 1854. 8°, pp. 25.
1,000 copies.

BAYARD, WM. Comments on the Nebraska Bill, with Views on Slavery, in contrast with Freedom; respectfully addressed to the Free States, by one acquainted with Southern Institutions. 8°, pp. 58.
Two editions of 1,000 copies each,

BOWDISH, JOHN. Annual Report of the Supervisors, Montgomery county. 8°, pp. 4.

BULLARD, GEN. Temperance and Popery: an Address delivered before the Saratoga County Convention, at Ballston Spa, Oct. 10, 1854. 8°, pp. 10.
1,000 copies.

By-Laws of the Medical Society of the State of New York, with the Rules of Order, Medical Ethics, etc. 8°, pp. 42.

Carrier's Address to the Patrons of the Albany Daily State Register. 8°, pp. 4.
  1,800 copies.

Cases and Points in the Court of Appeals of the State of New York. 8°.

Catalogue and Circular of the Albany Medical College, Spring Term, 1854. 8°, pp. 16.
  10,000 copies.

Catalogue of Books in the Cohoes District School Library. 12°, pp. 31.
  200 copies.

Catalogue of Books in the Library of the Second R. P. Dutch Church, Albany, N. Y. 12°, pp. 8.

Catalogue of Stationery, and Blank Books for sale by Edwin C. Little, Stationer and Blank Book Manufacturer, No 31 State Street, in Museum Building, corner of Broadway and State street. 18°, pp. 8.

Catalogue of the Officers and Students of Carlisle Seminary for 1854. 8°, pp. 16.
  350 copies.

Catalogue of the Trustees, Instructors and Students of Gilbertsville Academy and Collegiate Institute, Gilbertsville, Otsego County, N. Y. July, 1854. 8°, pp. 16.

Census of Attendance at all the places of Public Worship and Protestant Evangelical Sabbath Schools in Albany.   8°, pp. 4.
  It is believed that this was not issued to the public.

Circular and Catalogue of the Law School of the University of Albany, for the year 1854. 8°, pp. 16.

Cone, Solomon. The Harmonia ; a new Collection of Easy Songs, composed and arranged for one, two, three, and four Voices, with a new set of Rules and Practical Exercises, upon an original and Scientific Plan, for the use of Schools, Singing Classes, and Social Circles. Oblong 12°, 136.

Confession of Faith and Form of Covenant of the First Presbyterian Church in Valatie ; adopted June 5, 1852. 12°, pp. 12.
  800 copies.

Constitution, Act of Incorporation, and By-Laws of the Orphan Asylum, Albany. 12°, pp. 12.
  500 copies.

Constitution and By-Laws of Philmont Lodge, No. 91, of the Independent Order of Good Templars, located at Philmont, N. Y. Adopted 1854. 18°. pp. 20.
  200 copies.

CONSTITUTION and By-Laws of Star of Hope Lodge No. 433, I. O. of O. F. of the State of New York; instituted March 11, 1852. 18°, pp. 36.
100 copies.

CONSTITUTION and By-Laws of the Albany Methodist Sunday School Union, auxiliary to the Sunday School Union of the Methodist Episcopal Church; organized June 19, 1854. 12°, pp. 11.

CONSTITUTION and By-Laws of the Carroll Corps; adopted Nov., 1853; Corps organized 1853. 18°, pp. 12.

CONSTITUTION and By-Laws of the Catholic Young Men's Association, attached to St. Joseph's Church, Albany; organized with the approbation of the Very Rev. J. J. Conroy, Feb. 4, 1854. 18°, pp. 14.
200 copies.

CONSTITUTION and By-Laws of Tivoli Temple of Honor, No. 22, of the State of New York; instituted March, 1846; Place of Meeting 54 State Street, Albany. 18°, pp. 24.

CONSTITUTION, By-Laws and Catalogue of the Wesleyan Literary Association, Charlotteville, Schoharie Co., N. Y.   Revised Edition.   12°, pp. 16.
500 copies.

DIRECTORS of the Albany and Susquehanna Rail Road Company to the Stockholders and Memorialists. 8°, pp. 12.
3,000 copies.

DRAFT of a Bill for the Suppression of the Traffic in Intoxicating Liquors, reported by a committee appointed by the New York State Temperance Convention, Jan., 1853. 8°, pp. 14.

DUVALL, EDWARD. [Eugene Andrews.] The Secret of Alchemy, or the Grand Doctrine of Transmutation, fully and faithfully Explained. Together with the New Means of a Scientific application of the Powers of Nature for the Amelioration of nearly all kinds of Human Industry, or a Paradise without Labor, in which Mankind's Jubilee is fully demonstrated by Chemical and Scientific Analysis; the grand old Doctrine of the Cabalists, the Jews, Persians, Hebrews, Egyptians, Chinese, Tartars, Romans, &c., entitled The Cabala, or Natural and Celestial Magic, fully Explained. The whole embracing the most Rare and Important Mass of Knowledge yet given to Mankind, &c. 18°, pp. 303.
2,000 copies.

EIGHTEENTH Annual Report of the Albany City Tract Society, presented at the Annual Meeting in the Baptist Church, North Pearl Street, Dec. 25, 1854. 8°, pp. 27.
1,200 copies.

EVIDENCES in Favor of the South Route, gathered from the Official Report of A. F. Edwards, Chief Engineer of the Sackets Harbor and Saratoga Rail Road Company, dated Oct., 1853, and published March, 1854, with Extracts from the same. 8°, pp. 8.

EXERCISES of the Alumnæ of the Albany Female Academy, on their Thirteenth Anniversary, June 20, 1854. 8°, pp. 54.
400 copies.

EXTRACT from the Minutes of the General Assembly of the Presbyterian Church in the United States of America, convened at Philadelphia, May, 1854. 8°, pp. 8.

FIFTH Annual Report of the Inspectors of the Albany County Penitentiary made to the Board of Supervisors of the County of Albany, and the Mayor and Recorder of the City of Albany, in Joint Meeting assembled on the 16th day of December, 1853. Together with the Reports of the Superintendent, Chaplain and Physician of that Institution. 8°, pp. 40.
1,200 copies.

FIRST Anniversary Report of the Sabbath School and Missionary Association of the First Congregational Church, December 10, 1854. 12°, pp. 12.
500 copies.

FIRST Annual Catalogue of the Officers and Students of the Princetown Academy, Princetown, Schenectady Co., N. Y., December, 1854. 8°, pp. 24.
1,000 copies.

FORTY-THIRD Annual Report of the Albany County Bible Society, organized, A. D. 1810. 12°, pp. 15.
1,000 copies.

FOURTH Annual Application of John O'Brien, a Methodist of the New York Conference, for Redress, since rising of the Conference in May, 1850. 8°, pp. 22.
200 copies.

ELEVENTH Annual Report of the Albany City Missionary Society, presented May, 1854. 12°, pp. 12.
400 copies.

GREENWOOD, R. J. Descriptive Catalogue of the Bunyan Tableaux. 12°, pp. 38.
1,000 copies.

HARSHA, D. A. Wanderings of a Pilgrim; or, the Christian's Journey through the Wilderness of this World to the Heavenly Canaan. 32°, pp. 126.
600 copies.

HOUGH, FRANKLIN B. A History of Jefferson County in the State of New York; from the Earliest Period to the Present Time. 8°, pp. 601.
1,500 copies.

HUDSON Classis. Rules of Order of the Classis, Hudson. 12°,
200 copies.

JOURNAL of the Seventeenth Annual Session of the Franckean Evangelic Lutheran Synod, convened at Black Lake, St. Lawrence Co., N. Y., June 1, 1854. 8°, pp. 20.
500 copies.

LETTER on the Divinity of Christ, from a Father to his Son. 8°, pp. 18.
By John Fine.

LIGHTON, WILLIAM BEEBEY. Autobigraphy and Reminiscences of William Beebey Lighton, containing an Interesting and Faithful Account of his Early Life, Enlistment into the British Army, his Desertion, Capture, and Condemnation to Death, Sufferings, Escape from Prison, Settlement in the United States, and subsequent Career, written by himself. 12°, pp. xi, 311.

LITTLE, W. C.   Auction Sale of Books to reduce Stock.   8°.
750 copies.

LOVERIDGE, G.   A General Analysis to aid in the Review of Wood's Class Book of Botany, for the use of Academies and Schools.   18°, pp. 22.

MILLS, D. W.   The Banking Laws of the State of New York, complete, from the Original Law of 1838 to the close of the Session of 1854, in relation to Banks, Banking Associations, and Individual Bankers doing business under the same; arranged in the order in which they were passed, with marginal notes and references, together with an extract from the Constitution of the State of New York, adopted in 1846.   8°, pp. 76.
600 copies.

MINUTES of the Fifty-Ninth Session of the Evangelical Lutheran Ministerium of the State of New York, and adjacent States and Countries, held at Buffalo, Erie county, N. Y., Aug. 26 to Aug. 30, 1854.   8°, pp. 38.
500 copies.

MINUTES of the Particular Synod of Albany, convened in Regular Session in the North Ref. Dutch Church of West Troy, May 3, 1854.   8°, pp. 34.
200 copies.

MINUTES of the Twenty-fourth Annual Session of the Hartwick Synod of the Evangelical Lutheran Church in the State of New York, convened at Dansville, Livingston County, N. Y., Sept. 2, 1854.   8°, pp. 32.
500 copies.

MINORITY Report of the Rail Road Committee, on the Sackets Harbor and Saratoga Rail Road, and Letters in relation thereto.   8°, pp. 8.

MORRIS and KELLY.   Address delivered at the Annual Meeting of the New York State Agricultural Society, at Albany, February 9, 1854, by Lewis G. Morris, President, and William Kelly, on taking the chair as President elect.   8°, pp. 16.
200 copies.

[MUNSELL, JOEL.]   Cases of Personal Identity.   8°, pp. 102.
100 copies.

MUNSELL, JOEL.   Munsell's Albany Directory and City Register for 1854.   12°, pp. 492.
1,000 copies.

MUNSELL, J.   The Annals of Albany.   Vol. V.   12°, pp. 359.
500 copies.

MUNSELL, JOEL. Webster's Calendar, or the Albany Almanac for the year of our Lord 1855. 12°, pp. 36.
30,000 copies.

NILES. Sermon. 8°, pp. 23.
600 copies.

OFFICIAL Documents abridged on the Subject of the Sackets Harbor and Saratoga Rail Road, together with the Minority Report against changing the Route of said Road. 8°, pp. 23.

PARKES, STEPHEN. Troy Conference Miscellany, containing a Historical Sketch of Methodism within the Borders of the Troy Conference of the Methodist Episcopal Church, with Reminiscences of its deceased, and Contributions by its Living Ministers. With an Appendix. 12°, pp. 423.
2,500 copies.

PATERSON, JOHN. A Preceptor for the Violin : with a collection of Airs, Duetts, Marches, Dances, etc. 12th edition. Oblong 4°, pp. 52.
500 copies.

PROCEEDINGS of the Homœopathic Medical Society of the State of New York, 1853–54. 8°, pp. 45.
1,500 copies.

RATHBONE & KENNEDY, Stove Manufacturers, Office Nos. 9 and 11 Green Street ; Foundery North Ferry Street, Albany. 8°, pp. 55.
4,400 copies.

RAWSON, T. R. Eleventh Annual Report of the Albany Missionary Society, presented May, 1854. 12°, pp. 12.

REPLY to the Argument of John C: Spencer, Esq., presented before the Committee of the Senate appointed to investigate the affairs of Union College, in refutation of Certain Charges made therein. 8°, pp. 8.

REPORT of Gilbert S. Wilson, special agent appointed by D. B. St. John, Superintendent of the Bank Department, to examine into the affairs of the Merchants and Mechanics' Bank of Oswego. 8°, pp. 11.
600 copies.

REPORT of the Board of Managers of the Albany Bethel Church. 12°, pp. 4.

REPORT of the Committee of the Classis of Albany on Ministerial Support. 8°, pp. 41.
1,000 copies.

REPORT of the Special Committee in the Matter of the Application of the Northern Rail Road Company for Relief, made in Common Council, Feb. 23, 1854. 8°, pp. 32.
500 copies.

[RICH.] The English Universities in the North America Review, an Essay, by a LL. B. of Harvard College, sometime a Cmmoner of Magdalen Hall, Oxford. 8°, pp. 34.
300 copies.

SECOND Concert of Ancient Sacred Music in the Congregational Church, Albany, Tuesday Evening, March 28, 1854. 8°, pp. 4.

SELDEN, HENRY R. Reports of Cases argued and determined in the Court of Appeals of the State of New York; with Notes, References and an Index. Vol. III. 8°, pp. 606.
500 copies.

SIMMONS, GEORGE F. Faith in Christ the Condition of Salvation; a Sermon. 8°, pp. 15.

SOME Remarks on the Prospects of the Albany and Susquehanna Rail Road as a Dividend Paying Road. 8°, pp. 33.
1,000 copies.

STATEMENT Relating to the Double Wharfage collected at the City of Albany, and Explanatory of the Bill now before the Legislature. 8°, pp. 4.

STEVENS, SAMUEL. Catalogue of the valuable Law Library collected by the late Samuel Stevens, Esq., of the City of Albany. 8°, pp. 16.
50 copies.

TABER's Bill for the Incorporation of Roman Catholic Bishops. 8°, pp. 3.

TOWNSEND, JOHN F. Relations between the Professions of Law and Medicine. 8°, pp. 20.
500 copies.

TWENTY-THIRD Anniversary of the Stephentown Baptist Association, held in the Meeting house of the Baptist Church at East Chatham, Sept. 13 and 14, 1854. 8°, pp. 16.

VALENTINE, T. W. The New York Teacher, a Monthly Periodical, devoted to the Cause of General Education, but designed particularly as the Organ of the Teachers' Association of the State of New York. Vol. II. 8°, pp. 390.
1,700 copies.

WELLS, G. C. Narrative and Reflections of Justin Wells, compiled from Manuscripts written by Himself. Fourth edition. 18°, pp. 96.
1,000 copies.

WENDELL, JOHN L. Reports of Cases argued and determined in the Supreme Court of Judicature and in the Court for the Trial of Impeachments and the Correction of Errors of the State of New York. Vol. IV. 2d Edition, with Notes and References embracing the subsequent Decisions. 8°, pp. 709.
275 copies.

WENDELL, JOHN L. Reports of Cases argued and determined in the Supreme Court of Judicature, and in the Court for the Trial of Impeachments and the Correction of Errors of the State of New York. Vol. VII, with notes and references by Robert Johnstone. 8°, pp. viii, 698.
250 copies.

WENDELL, JOHN L. Reports of Cases argued and determined in the Supreme Court of Judicature, and in the Court for the Trial of Impeachments and the Correction of Errors of the State of New York. Vol. VIII, with Notes and References embracing the subsequent Cases. 8°, pp. 427.
250 copies.

WENDELL, JOHN L. Reports of Cases argued and determined in the Supreme Court of Judicature and in the Court for the Trial of Impeachments and the Correction of Errors of the State of New York. Vol. IX, 2d edition, with Notes and References, including all the subsequent Decisions. 8°, pp, viii. 705.
250 copies.

WISE, ISAAC M. History of the Israelitish Nation, from Abraham to the Present Time, derived from the original sources. Vol. I. (all that was printed.) 8°, pp. xxiv, 560.
2,000 copies.

WOOD, JEREMIAH. The Model Pastor. The Life and Character of the Rev. Elisha Yale, D. D., late of Kingsboro', drawn mostly from his own Diary and Correspondence: together with the Discourse preached at his Funeral, Jan. 13, 1853. 12°, pp. 384.
1,000 copies.

WOOLLETT, WM. L. Plans and Description of Grounds and Building of the New York Asylum for Idiots, erected at Syracuse. 8°, pp. 8.
400 copies.

1855.

ADDRESS of the Carriers of the Albany Morning Express to its Patrons. 8°, pp. 8.
900 copies.

ALBANY Morning Express. Folio.
Daily Newspaper.

AMES, JULIUS. Spirit of Humanity, and the Animal's Friend; extracted from the Productions of the Enlightened and Benevolent of various Ages and Climes. 8°, pp. 286.
1,000 copies.

ANNUAL Catalogue of the Officers and Students of Hartwick Theological and Classical Seminary, for the Academic Year ending August 29, 1855. 8°, pp. 12.

ARTICLES of Association and By-Laws of the New Baltimore Mutual Insurance Association. 18°, pp. 16.

BATE, JOHN. The Christian's Self-Examiner or 365 Questions for Self-Examination, being one for every day in the year, with an appropriate passage of Scripture. 32°, pp. 128.
1,500 copies.

BIENNIAL Report of the Executive Committee of the Foreign Missionary Society of the Evangelical Lutheran Church in the United States, presented at Dayton, Ohio, June, 1855. 8°, pp. 24.
500 copies.

BOWEN, TRUMAN H. The New York Teacher, a Monthly Periodical, devoted to the Cause of General Education, and particularly to the Elevation of the Teachers' Profession. Vol. III, pp. 396; vol. IV, pp. 376.
5,000 copies.

BUGBEE, L. H. The Artist: An Address delivered before the Athenia Society of the Cooperstown Seminary and Female Collegiate Institute, April 4, 1855. 8°, pp. 32.

CASES and Points in the Supreme Court of the State of New York. 8°, 3 vols.
20 copies.

CATALOGUE and Circular of the Albany Medical College, Spring Term, 1855. 8°, pp. 16.
5,000 copies.

CATALOGUE and Circular of the Young Ladies Institute, No 4 High Street, nearly opposite the Capitol, Albany, N. Y. 8°, pp. 12.
200 copies.

CATALOGUE of Books in the Sabbath School Library of the Pearl Street Baptist Church. 18°, pp. 20.
100 copies.

CATALOGUE of New Law Blanks published and for sale by Fisk & Little, No 82 State street, Albany, N. Y. 12°, pp. 8.

CATALOGUE of 174 Oil Paintings. 8°, pp. 9.

CATALOGUE of the Cooperstown Seminary and Female Collegiate Institute, for first two Terms ending April 10, 1855. 8°, pp. 39.
3,000 copies.

CATALOGUE of the Officers and Students of Monroe Academy, at Elbridge, Onondaga County, N. Y., for the Academic year, 1854–55. 8°, pp. 16.
500 copies. Plate.

CATECHISM for the use of Evangelical Lutheran Churches. 18°, pp. 38.
1,050 copies.

CIRCULAR and Catalogue of the Albany Female Academy, founded A. D. 1814, incorporated Feb. 16, 1821. 8°, pp. 21.
500 copies.

CIRCULAR and Catalogue of the Law School of the University of Albany for the year 1854–5. 8°, pp. 16.
3,000 copies.

CONFESSION of Faith of the Second Baptist Church of Galway, Saratoga County, N. Y. 18°, pp. 18.

CONSTITUTION and By-Laws of the Albany Sunday School Union, organized Feb. 14, 1853. 12°, pp. 8.
750 copies.

CONSTITUTION, By-Laws and Rules of Order of Evening Star Encampment, No. 32, I. O. of O. F. of the State of New York, held in the Town of Chatham, by Authority of a Charter from the Grand Encampment of the State of New York ; instituted Feb. 20, 1851. 18°, pp. 30.
500 copies.

CONSTITUTION of the Hillsdale Mercantile Association, organized Jan. 1, 1855. 12°, pp. 8.
100 copies.

CONSTITUTION of the O. U. A. and Laws of Arch-Chancery, together with the By-Laws of Star Spangled Banner Chapter No. 56, Albany, N. Y., 18°, pp. 36.
500 copies.

DUER, JOHN.   Reports of Cases argued and determined in the Superior Court of the City of New York. Vol. II.   8°, pp. 717.
1,000 copies.

EMMONS, EBENEZER.   American Geology, containing a Statement of the Principles of the Science, with full Illustrations of the Characteristic American Fossils ; with an Atlas and a Geological Map of the United States. Vol. I. 8°, pp. 251.
960 copies.

EXERCISES of the Alumnæ of the Albany Female Academy, on their Fourteenth Anniversary, June 21, 1855. 8°, pp. 52.
400 copies.

FIRST Annual Catalogue of the Washington County Seminary and Collegiate Institute, Fort Edward, N. Y., from Dec., 1854 to Nov., 1855. 8°, pp. 40.
3,000 copies.

FORTY-FOURTH Annual Report of the Albany County Bible Society, organized A. D. 1810. 12°, pp. 15.
1,000 copies.

HAWLEY, GIDEON.   An Essay on the Definitions of Knowledge and Truth. 8°, pp. 61.
100 copies. This was increased to 67 pages, and was then the final edition, instead of the one mentioned before.

HERR, RUDOLPH.   The Jeweler's Hand Book, containing Thirty Practical Methods for Galvanizing, Electro-Plating and Coloring with Gold, Silver and Copper, on all kinds of Metals, without any Apparatus, and by means of Single and Combined Elements of Batteries, with an extra Chapter showing the Recovery of the Gold and Silver. Practically demonstrated and embellished with six Engravings. 12°, pp. 108.
500 copies.

HOME, Sweet Home. 12°, pp. 236.
2,000 copies.

HUNTINGTON, REV. E. A. Last words of a Pastor to his People. Two Discourses delivered to the Third Presbyterian Church, Albany, Dec. 31, 1854 and Jan. 7, 1855, the last two Sabbaths of a Ministry of Eighteen years ; with a History of the Third Presbyterian Church, Albany. 8°, pp. 102.
500 copies.

IN MEMORIAM ; Eliza Hale Paine entered into Rest May 31, 1855. 8°, pp. 75.
100 copies.

JOHNSON, WILLIAM. Reports of Cases argued in the Court of Chancery of New York. Vol. V, containing Cases argued from December, 1820, to December 1821, inclusive. Second Edition, Revised and Corrected. 8°, pp. 606.

JONES, R. D. Opening Address before the New York State Teachers' Association, at Utica, Wednesday, Aug. 1, 1855. 8°, pp. 12.
300 copies.

JORDAN and NORTON. Catalogue of one hundred Cases of English Books 8°, pp. 32.
500 copies.

KELLY and CHEEVER. Address delivered before the New York State Agricultural Society, at the Annual Meeting at Albany, Feb, 15, 1855, by Wm. Kelly, President; and the address of Samuel Cheever, on taking the Chair as President elect. 8°, pp. 24.
300 copies.

LAW Cases. 8°.

LAWS relating to the Incorporation of Villages, and the By-Laws of the Village of Cohoes. 8°, pp. 68.
200 copies.

LIST of Officers, Committees and Judges, Constitution and By-Laws, List of Premiums, Rules and Regulations, of the Albany County Agricultural Society for 1855. 8°, pp. 38.
2,000 copies.

MAHAN, M. The Healing of the Nations ; a Sermon, preached in St. Peter's Church, Albany, on Thanksgiving Day, Nov. 29, 1855. 8°, pp. 22.
600 copies.

MEADS, ORLANDO. An Address to the Class of Graduates of the Albany Medical College, delivered Dec. 26, 1854. 8°, pp. 20.
500 copies.

MINUTES of the Fifty-ninth Anniversary of the Rensselaerville Association, held in the Meeting House of the Baptist Church in Berne and Knox, commencing Sept. 19, 1855. 8°, pp. 16.
750 copies.

MINUTES of the Particular Synod of Albany, convened in Regular Session in the 1st Reformed Dutch Church of Schenectady, May 2, 1855. 8°, pp. 37.
250 copies

MINUTES of the Sixtieth Synod of the Evangelical Lutheran Ministerium of the State of New York, and Adjacent States and Countries, held at Churchtown, Columbia Co., N. Y., Sept. 1 to Sept. 5, 1855. 8°, pp. 40.
500 copies.

MINUTES of the Thirty-seventh Annual Session of the N. Y. Eastern Christian Conference, held in Stamfordville, Dutchess County, N. Y., on the 2d, 4th, and 5th of June, 1855. 12°, pp. 12.

MINUTES of the Twenty-fifth Annual Session of the Hartwick Synod of the Evangelical Lutheran Church in the State of New York, convened at Guilderland, Albany County, New York, Sept. 8 to 12th, 1855. 8°, pp. 35.
500 copies.

MISSIONARY Convocation of Northern New York; Church Building Committee. 12°, pp. 12.

[MUNSELL, JOEL.] Munsell's Albany Directory and City Register for 1855. 12°, pp. 465.
1,200 copies.

MUNSELL, J. The Annals of Albany. Vol. VI. 12°, pp. 359.
500 copies.

MUNSELL. Webster's Calendar, or the Albany Almanac for the year of our Lord 1856. 12°, pp. 36.

MUSIC Reader's Companion. 8°, pp. 8.

NINETEENTH Annual Report of the Albany City Tract Society, presented at the Annual Meeting in the Second Presbyterian Church, Dec. 24, 1854. 8°, pp. 26.
1,000 copies.

OPINIONS of the American Press in the various Cities in which Mrs. Macready has performed. 12°, pp. 36.

PARKER, AMASA J. Reports of Decisions in Criminal Cases made at Term, at Chambers and in the Courts of Oyer and Terminer of the State of New York. Vol. I. 8°, pp. 716.

PHELPS, WILLIAM F. Address delivered before the Association of Graduates of the State Normal School at Albany, Thursday, July 12, 1855. 8°, pp. 10.
300 copies.

[PHŒNICIAN Inscription.] 8°, pp. 2.
This accompanied a fac simile inscription which was found upon the sarcophagus of Esmunazar, king of Sidon, and was the largest portion of Phœnician that had thus far been found anywhere. It was carefully copied for the Albany Institute by the missionary Van Dyck, and its dissemination by the Institute took the learned world by surprise. It was more fully published in the Institute Transactions, vol. IV.

PRICE List and Drawings of Axes and Edge Tools manufactured by D. Simmons & Company, at Cohoes, N. Y. 12°, pp. 21.
1,000 copies.

PROCEEDINGS of the Forty-Second Anniversary of the Washington County Bible Society, and other Anniversaries of Benevolent Associations, held at Salem, N. Y. 12°, pp. 26.
800 copies.

PROCEEDINGS of the Forty-Third Anniversary of the Washington County Bible Society, and Anniversaries of Benevolent Associations, held at Whitehall, Sept. 5th and 6th, 1855. 12°, pp. 24.
1,000 copies.

PUBLIC Schools in Albany, inadequate to meet the wants of the Public; and the necessity of Reform. 8°, pp. 23.
1,000 copies.

RATHBONE and KENNEDY, Stove Manufacturers, Office Nos. 9 and 11, Green Street, Foundery North Ferry Street, Albany, N. Y. 8°, pp. 49.
2,000 copies.

[RAWSON, T. R.] Twelfth Annual Report of the Albany Missionary Society, presented May, 1855. 12°, pp. 11.
400 copies.

REPORT of the Board of Commissioners of the District Schools of the City of Albany, to the Common Council, made Aug. 7, 1834. 8°, pp. 8.
500 copies.

REPORT of the Water Committee of the Common Council of the City of Albany, made Oct. 29, 1855, in accordance with a Resolution of Inquiry as to the Impure Water furnished the City west of Pearl Street, from the Bleeker Reservoir. 8°, pp. 26.
1,000 copies.

REPORT on Church Building Society. 12°, pp. 11.

RICE, V. M. Annual Report of the Superintendent of Public Instruction. 8°, pp. 26.

RICHMOND, JAMES. Petition to the Hon. Legislature of the State of New York. 8°, pp. 7.
700 copies.

ROSIN GAS. Reply of the Aubin Portable Gas Works Company to the Letter of Prof. Torreys of New York. 8°, pp. 16.

[SCHOOLCRAFT, HENRY R.] Helderbergia: an Apotheosis of the Anti Rent War. 8°, pp. 54.
300 copies.

SCOTT, DAVID B. Where do we stand: An Address before the New York State Teachers' Association, at Utica, Thursday, Aug. 2, 1855.
300 copies.

SELDEN, HENRY R. Reports of Cases argued and determined in the Court of Appeals of the State of New York, with Notes, References and an Index. Vol. IV. 8°, pp. 591.

SIXTH Annual Report of the Inspectors of the Albany Penitentiary. 8°, pp. 49.
     1,200 copies. Not on file.

SPECIFICATIONS for the Construction of an Elliptical Brick Sewer in Lydius Street, from South Pearl to the River, about 1660 feet. 8°, pp. 7.

SPEECH of Hon E. Brooks on the Church Property Bill. 8°, pp. 17.
     2,500 copies.

SPEECH of Hon. J. R. Rhodes, of Kings County, in the Assembly, Feb. 24, 1855, on the Resolution requiring a residence of twenty-one years, before Naturalization. 8°, pp. 3.
     1,000 copies.

STATE Normal School; twenty-first Term, Thursday, Feb. 1, 1855. 8°, pp. 4.

TALLMADGE, S. W. Tax-Payers Attention. 8°, pp. 8.

TIVOLI Hollow Ware Works: List of Tivoli Hollow Ware, made and sold by Winne & Abeel. 8°, pp. 24.

TOWNSEND, FRANKLIN. Pattern List of Townsend's Furnace and Machine Shop, Albany, N. Y., comprising a Catalogue of the Wheel and Pulley Patterns, and Racks and Roll Chills, attached to that Establishment, and also an Appendix containing Tables of Useful Calculations. Third Edition. Cap 8°, pp. 161.
     500 copies.

TRINITY Church Title. Letter Sheet, pp. 3.

VISIT to Philadelphia of Tivoli Hose Company of Albany, N. Y., as the Guests of Columbia Hose Company, on the Second day of October, A. D. 1854. 18°, pp. 28.
     500 copies.

WENDELL, JOHN L. Reports of Cases, argued and determined in the Supreme Court of Judicature, and the Court for the Correction of Errors of the State of New York. 8°, pp. viii, 698.

WOOD, D. Alligation. 8°, pp. 8.
     300 copies.

[WOOD, GEORGE.] Transactions of the Albany Institute. Vol. III. 8°, pp. 454.
     300 copies.

YALE, ELISHA. The Pastor's Farewell; two Sermons preached at Kingsboro, N. Y., June 27th, 1852, upon the Resignation of his charge as Pastor of the Church at that Place. 8°, pp. 31.
     500 copies.

1856.

ADDRESS by the Directors of the Albany and Susquehanna Rail Road Company, together with the Law authorizing Town Subscriptions, April, 1856. 8°, pp. 16.

ADDRESS of the Carriers of the Albany Morning Express to its Patrons. 8°, pp. 7.

ALBANY Daily Statesman. Folio.
  Daily newspaper, published in the interest of the American or *Know Nothing* party, to advocate the reëlection of Millard Fillmore to the presidency of the United States. Edited by Alexander Mann and C. D. Brigham.

ANNUAL Catalogue of the Officers and Students of Hartwick Theological and Classical Seminary, for the Academic year ending August 27, 1858. 8°, pp. 12.

ANNUAL Report of the Superintendent of the Sabbath School connected with the Presbyterian Church at Cooperstown, N. Y., Sept. 28, 1856. 8°, pp. 10.

ANNUAL Report of the Albany Guardian Society and Home for the Friendless, for the years 1854 and 1855. 12°, pp. 22.
  200 copies.

ANNUAL Report of the Bible Society. 12°, pp. 17.
  1,000 copies.

ASSIGNEES Sale of assigned Effects of Geo. Hepinstall. 8°, pp. 6.

BEMAN, N. S. S. Episcopacy Exclusive : or, two Series of Letters, being a Review of Dr. Coit's Sermon and Pamphlet. 8°, pp. 102.
  1,000 copies.

BENTON, NATHANIEL S. A History of Herkimer County, including the Upper Mohawk Valley, from the Earliest Period to the Present Time; with a Brief Notice of the Iroquois Indians, the Early German Tribes, the Palatine Immigrations into the Colony of New York, and Biographical Sketches of the Palatine Families, the Patentees of Burnets field in 1725: also Biographical Notices of the most Prominent Public Men of the County: with important Statistical Information. 8°, pp. 497.
  1,000 copies.

BIBLE Class Lesson, repeated at the Tabernacle May 9, 1856, by the Scholars of the Five Points Ladies Mission School. 16°, pp. 16.

BLAKE and KEWIN ; Catalogue Sale of Hardware, Cutlery, &c., at Auction, on Wednesday, Nov. 5th. 12°, pp. 12.

CATALOGUE and Circular of the Albany Medical College, Spring Term, 1856. 8°, pp. 16.
  4,500 copies. 2 Plates.

CATALOGUE and Circular of the Young Ladies' Institute, No. 4 High Street, nearly opposite the Capitol, Albany, N. Y. 8°, pp. 12.

CATALOGUE and Price List of Articles Sold by Henderson, Kennedy and Kneeland, 312 and 314 Broadway, Albany, N. Y. 18°, pp. 56.

CATALOGUE of a Part of the Library of the late Dr. T. Romeyn Beck, offered for sale at the prices affixed. 8°, pp. 19.

CATALOGUE of Books in the Library of the Rensselaer Street Mission Sunday School. 18°, pp. 20.

CATALOGUE of Johnstown Academy for the Academic year, 1855–6. 8°, pp. 12.
500 copies.

CATALOGUE of John C. Spencer's Library. 8°, pp. 16.
300 copies.

CATALOGUE of the Corporation, Officers and Students of Lowville Academy, Lowville, N. Y., for the Academic year ending Aug. 1, 1856. 8°, pp. 30.
800 copies.

CATALOGUE of the Officers and Students of Schoharie Academy, during the year ending April 14th, 1856. 8°, pp, 16.
400 copies.

CATALOGUE of the Palmer Marbles, at the Hall belonging to the Church of Divine Unity, 548 Broadway, New York, November, 1856. 8°, pp. 20.
1,000 copies.

CHEEVER, SAMUEL. Address delivered before the New York State Agricultural Society at its Annual Meeting at Albany, Feb. 15, 1856. 8°, pp. 30.
1,000 copies.

CIRCULAR and Catalogue of the Albany Female Academy, founded A. D. 1814, incorporated Feb. 16, 1821. 8°, pp. 19.
5,000 copies.

CIRCULAR and Catalogue of the Law School of the University of Albany, for the year 1856. 8°, pp. 16.
6,000 copies.

CIRCULAR of the State University of Iowa, located at Iowa City, Iowa. 8°, pp. 16.

CLARK, F. J. Dental Monitor: or Remarks on the Proper Management of the Teeth; giving a Synopsis of Operations, properly performed. 12°, pp. 24.

CLINTON, GEORGE W. An Address delivered at the closing Exercises of the Twenty-Third Term of the Normal School of the State of New York, July 10, 1856. 8°, pp. 16.
1,000 copies.

CONCERT of the Hudson Female Academy. 8°, pp. 4.
500 copies.

CONSTITUTION and By-Laws of the Brotherhood of the Protestant Episcopal Church in the Diocese of New York. 18°, pp. 7.

CONSTITUTION and By-Laws of the First Baptist Sabbath School and Judson Missionary Society, of the City of Albany, and the Catalogues of the Teachers and Scholars Libraries. 12°, pp. 24.
500 copies.

CONSTITUTION and By-Laws of Putnam Hose Company No. 3; adopted Nov. 13, 1855. 18°, pp. 11.

CONSTITUTION of the Evangelical Lutheran Ministerium of the State of New York, and adjacent States and Countries; revised and adopted in General Synod, Sept. 3, A. D. 1816. Third Edition. 12°, pp. 24.
500 copies.

DELAVAN, EDWARD C. Speech. 8°.
112,000 copies. Campaign document.

DEMAREST, DAVID D. Religion in Politics; a Sermon preached in the Reformed Dutch Church of Hudson, N. Y., July 6, and repeated by Request, July 13. 8°, pp. 16.

EXERCISES of the Alumnæ of the Albany Female Academy, on their Fifteenth Anniversary, June 24, 1856. 8°, pp. 60.
350 copies.

FANNIE, AUNT. Home, Sweet Home: a Holiday Gift for Children, or Recollections of my youthful Days. 16°, pp. 236.

FILMORE, MILLARD. Speeches. 8°, pp.
10,600 copies. Campaign document.

FOR Sale a Tract of 350 Acres of Timber Land, with Saw Mill, Shingle Machine and Machinery, having a plank road passing diagonally through the same. 8°, pp. 4.

FORTY-EIGHTH Annual Report of the Baptist Missionary Convention of the State of New York, held with the Baptist Church in Binghamton, October 10, 11, 12, 1855. 8°, pp. 60.
1,500 copies.

FORTY-FIFTH Annual Report of the Albany County Bible Society. 12°, pp. 15.

GOWANS, WILLIAM. Catalogue of New English and American Books, at greatly reduced prices. 8°, pp. 24.
500 copies.

GREENWOOD, R. J. A Descriptive Catalogue of the Bunyan Tableaux. 15°, pp. 36.
1,000 copies.

HALL, JAMES. Description of New Species of Fossils, from the Carboniferous Limestones of Indiana and Illinois. Also Descriptions of New Organic Remains, from the Cretaceous Rocks of Vancouver's Island, by F. B. Meek. 8°, pp. 49.

HALL, W. C. Catalogues of Books. 8°, pp. 30, 24.
1,500 copies.

HAWLEY, GIDEON. An Essay on Knowledge, chiefly with a view to its Definition and Division. 8°, pp. 25.
20 copies. 229 pages printed.

HILL, WILLIAM. A Father's Legacy. 18°, pp. 40.
2,000 copies.

HILL, WILLIAM. The Rise and Fall of the Jews. 18°, pp. 40.
2,000 copies.

HOUGH, FRANKLIN B. Papers relating to the Island of Nantucket, with Documents relating to the original settlement of that Island, Martha's Vineyard, and other Islands adjacent, known as Dukes County, while under the Colony of New York. Compiled from Official Records in the Office of Secretary of State at Albany, New York. Cap 4to, pp. xviii, 162.

HURST, J. F. Why Americans love Shakespeare : an Address. 8°, pp. 15.

IN the Supreme Court of the State of New York ; the Albany Northern Rail Road Company, Erastus Corning and Andrew White, Trustees and Receivers, &c., against Isaac Brownell and Albert Brown, Commissioners of Highways of the Town of Hoosick in the County of Rensselaer. 8°, pp. 27.

J. C. FREMONT's Record. 8°, pp. 16.
310,000 copies. Campaign document.

JESSUP. Agricultural Address. 8°, pp. 23.
200 copies.

JOURNAL of the Nineteenth Annual Session of the Franckean Evangelic Lutheran Synod, convened at Clay, Onondaga Co., N. Y., June 5, 1856 8°, pp. 26.
500 copies.

KIRCHENORDNUNG der Ersten Deutschen Evangelisch-Lutherischen Kirche zu Albany, N. Y., ecke von Franklin-und Nucella-Strassen, unter der Aufsicht des Pastors T. F. W. Rechenberg. 12°, pp. 8.
500 copies.

LAWS of the State of New York, passed at the Seventy-ninth Session of the Legislature, begun January first and ended April ninth, 1856, in the City of Albany. 8°, pp. 392.

LAZARUS in Abraham's Bosom. 12°, pp. 8.
1,000 copies.

LEE's Speeches. 8°, pp.
10,000 copies. Campaign document.

LETTER from the Hon. Daniel D. Barnard, addressed to James A. Hamilton, Esq., on the Political Condition of the Country and the State of Parties, and in Favor of Millard Fillmore for President. 8°, pp. 16.
10,000 copies. Campaign document.

LIST of Premiums, Officers, Committees and Judges, Constitution, By-Laws, Rules and Regulations of the Albany County Agricultural Society, for 1856. 8°, pp. 40.
3,000 copies.

McCoy and CLARK, Stove Manufacturers, Office Nos. 13 and 15 Green Street; Foundery, Montgomery Street, Albany, N. Y. 8°, pp. 39.
1,000 copies.

MINUTES of the General Association of New York, at their Meeting in Albany, October 14, 1856, together with the Narrative and Statistics of the Churches. 8°, pp. 45.

MINUTES of the General Conference of the State of New York. 8°, pp. 64.
500 copies.

MINUTES of the Particular Synod of Albany, convened in Regular Session in the 1st Reformed Dutch Church of Coxsackie, May 7, 1856. 8°, pp. 35.
250 copies.

MINUTES of the Presbyterian Synod. 8°, pp. 15.
1,000 copies.

MINUTES of the Sixtieth Anniversary of the Rensselaerville Association, held in the Meeting House of the Baptist Church in New Baltimore, commencing Sept. 17, 1856. 8°, pp. 16.

MINUTES of the Sixty-first Synod of the Evangelical Lutheran Ministerium of the State of New York, and Adjacent States and Countries, held at St. Luke's Church, Valatie, Columbia Co, N. Y., Sept 6 to Sept. 10, 1856. 8°, pp. 47.
650 copies.

MINUTES of the Stephentown Baptist Association. pp. 12.
400 copies.

MINUTES of the Thirty-eighth Annual Session of the New York Eastern Christian Conference, held at Charleston Four Corners, Montgomery Co., N. Y., May 29th, 30th, and 31st. 12°, pp. 22.
1,000 copies.

MINUTES of the Twenty-sixth Annual Session of Hartwick Synod of the Evangelical Lutheran Church in the State of New York, convened at Schoharie, N. Y., Sept. 13, 1856. 8°, pp. 32.
1,000 copies.

MUNSELL, JOEL. Catalogue of Bibliographical Library, offered for sale complete, at the prices affixed. 8°, pp. 38.

[MUNSELL, JOEL.] Munsell's Albany Directory and City Register, for 1856.
1,200 copies.

MUNSELL, J. Origin of Sunday Schools in Albany. 8°, pp. 23.
100 copies.

MUNSELL, J. Webster's Calendar, or the Albany Almanac for the year of our Lord 1857. 12°, pp. 36.

NORTHROP, R. H.   Report of the Superintendent of the Pioneer Mills Mine, Cabarrus County, N. C., Dec. 24, 1855.   8°, pp. 8.

PALMER, RAY.   Essays, Discourses and Miscellanies.   8°, pp. 4.
[Prospectus.]

PALMER, RAY.   Two Sermons.   8°, pp. 61.
1,250 copies.

PARKER, AMASA J.   Reports of Decisions in Criminal Cases made at Term, at Chambers, and in the Courts of Oyer and Terminer of the State of New York.   8°, pp. 710.
1,000 copies.

RAWSON, T. R.   Albany City Missionary Society ; Thirteenth Annual Report presented May, 1856.   12°, pp. 11.
400 copies.

REPORT of the Commissioners of the Albany Northern Rail Road Loan, made to the Common Council of the City of Albany, April 14, 1856. 8°, pp. 20.

REPORT of the Superintendent of Public Instruction, for the year 1856. 8°, pp. 23.

REPORT of the Water Committee on the Report of the Water Commissioners to the Common Council.   8°, pp. 15.
500 copies.

RICE, E. B.   Rules for Journalizing by Double Entry.   8°, pp. 16.

RULES and Regulations for the Government of Congregations recommended by the Evangelical Lutheran Ministerium of the State of New York; adopted at the Synod of 1852.   12°, pp. 14.
500 copies.

SAM HOUSTON'S Letter.   8°, pp. 4.
6,000 copies.   Campaign document.

SAMMONS.   Addresses.   8°, pp. 4.
158,000 copies.   Campaign document.

[SKERRITT, MISS.]   Catalogue and Circular of the Young Ladies' Institute No. 4 High Street, nearly opposite the Capitol, Albany, N. Y. Founded 1842.   8°, pp.

SEELYE, S. T.   A Sermon delivered in the Fourth Presbyterian Church, Albany, on Sabbath Morning, Oct. 5, 1856, commemorative of Susan D. Aikin, wife of Rev. Edward Aikin, of the Syrian Mission.   8°, pp. 31.
500 copies.

SPEECH of Hon. Erastus Brooks on an Agricultural College for the State of New York.   8°, pp. 8.
10,000 copies.   Campaign document.

STATUTEN des St. Petrus-Vereins in Albany ; mit Gutheissen des Hochwürdigsten Herrn Pfarrers der heiligen Kreuzkirche.   12°, pp. 16.

TALLMADGE, S. W.   The Rensselaer County Board of Supervisors Defence of Themselves.   8°, pp. 16.
1,000 copies.

TATOR, HENRY H. Eureka, a poem. 8°, pp. 15.
300 copies. This fellow's brain was sadly distorted, and this was a sample of the *method* of his madness.

TATOR, HENRY H. Hercules, a Poem in Four Books. 8°, pp. 55.
300 copies. He did not have money to redeem Hercules from the inexorable *press*, and the old hero went to the paper mill.

TRINITY Church Title: An Exposure of Miller's Letter with Documents, &c., addressed to the late Commissioners of the Land office. 8°, pp. 46.
2,000 copies.

TWENTIETH Annual Report of the Albany City Tract and Missionary Society, presented at the Annual Meeting in the First Presbyterian Church, Dec. 16, 1855. 8°, pp. 34.
1,200 copies.

VAN WORMER & MCGARVEY'S Price List and Pattern Sheet of Stoves for 1856. 16°, pp. 16.
300 copies.

WENDELL, JOHN L. Reports of Cases argued and determined in the Supreme Court of Judicature, and in the Court for the Correction of Errors of the State of New York. Vol. XVIII, 2d edition, with notes and references, by John J. Cole, counsellor at law. 8°, pp. vi, 707.

WENDELL, JOHN L. Reports of Cases argued and determined in the Supreme Court of Judicature, and in the Court for the Trial of Impeachments and the Correction of Errors in the State of New York, 2d edition, with additional notes and references by a member of the bar. 8°, pp. viii, 676.

WILDER, ALEXANDER. The New York Teacher: a monthly Periodical devoted to the Cause of General Education, and to the elevation of the Teachers' Profession. Vol. V, from Oct., 1855 to Sept., 1856. 8°, pp. viii, 584.
7,000 copies.

WRIGHT, NATHANIEL & Co. Price List: Manufacturers, Importers and Dealers in Coach and Saddlery Hardware, 324 Broadway, corner of Hamilton Street, Albany, N. Y. 18°, pp. 58.
1,000 copies.

WYCKOFF, I. N. Sermon occasioned by the Death of David Pruyn, delivered in the Second Reformed Protestant Dutch Church, Albany, Feb. 5, 1843. 8°, pp. 28.
250 copies.

WYCKOFF, ISAAC N. Sermon occasioned by the Death of Hibertie Pruyn, widow of the late David Pruyn; delivered in the Second Reformed Protestant Church, Albany, Sept. 30, 1855. 8°, pp. 43.

1857.

ADAMS, GEORGE. The Albany Directory, for the year 1857; containing a General Directory of the Citizens, a Business Directory, and other Miscellaneous Matter. 8°, pp. 198, 56.
2,000 copies.

ADAMS, GEORGE. The Troy Directory for the year 1857; with a Business Directory. and other Miscellaneous Matter; also Directories of West Troy and Green Island. 12°, pp. 340.
800 copies.

ADDRESS of the Carriers of the Albany Daily Statesman, to its Patrons, January 1, 1857. 8°, pp. 8.

ALBANY Daily Statesman. Folio.
Daily newspaper, having a circulation this second year of its publication, of 2,500 subscribers, and from 20,000 to 30,000 weekly, in aid of the campaign of the American party for the election of Mr. Fillmore. This was the largest distribution that had been known in this city at this time. On the defeat of the party in November, the circulation fell off to about 1,200 daily, and 2,000 weekly.

ALBANY Northern Rail Road Bonds: Opinion of Mr. Justice D. Wright, on an Application for an Injunction to restrain the Mayor, Aldermen, &c., of the City of Albany, from Paying the Interest on Bonds issued by them. 8°, pp. 19.
200 copies.

AMERICAN Party of New York; Address adopted at the Annual Meeting of the State Council, at Troy, Feb. 24th and 25th, 1857. 8°, pp. 8.

AN ACT revising, amending and consolidating the several acts in relation to the Charter of the Village of Greenbush, passed March 22, 1854, with the By-Laws of the Board of Trustees, adopted 1857. 8°, pp. 43.
300 copies.

ANNUAL Catalogue of the Officers and Students of Hartwick Theological and Classical Seminary, for the Academic year, ending Aug. 26, 1857. 8°, pp. 12.

ANNUAL Catalogue of the Officers and Students of the Sand Lake Collegiate Institute, Sand Lake, N. Y. 8°. pp. 16.

ANNUAL Report of the Directors of the Mutual Insurance Association of Nassau, Schodack and Chatham. 12°, pp. 12.

ANNUAL Report of the Managers of St. Paul's Church Home, for the year ending Dec. 31st, 1856. 12°, pp. 12.

ARTICLES of Association and By-Laws of the New York and Western Towing Company, together with the Act under which the Company is incorporated, and that Part of the Revised Statutes referred to therein. 8°, pp. 24.

ARTICLES of Association of the Bank of the Interior. 8°, pp. 10.

BAYLEY, JACOB ROOSEVELT. Statuta Novarcensis Diœceseos a reverend-
issimo domino Jacobo Roosevelt Bayley, Novarcensi Episcope, in
Synodo Diœcesano prima habita Mense Augusto, 1856, in Collegio Se-
ton-Hall, Madison, N. J., lata et promulgate. 12°, pp. 52.
100 copies.

BEECHER and CARTER. Catalogue of the Female Seminary, Saratoga. 8°,
pp. 22.
500 copies.

BELLINGER, HENRY. Substantie eener Predicatie, uitgesproken in New
York, den 22 Mei 1856. 8°, pp. 15.

BIENNIAL Reports Lutheran Foreign Mission Society. 8°, pp. 16.
500 copies.

BIGOT, JACQUES. Relation de ce qvi s'est passé de plvs remarqvable dans
la Mission Abnaquise de Sainct Joseph de Sillery, et dans l'Etablisse-
ment de la nouvelle Mission de Sainct Francois de Sales, l'année 1684.
8°, pp. 62.

BRIND, GEORGE. The True Philosophy of Vegetation, or its Primary
Principle explained ; showing the Origin of Carbon, and the Source from
whence we receive our Daily Supply of Vegetable Food ; with prescribed
Rules for Practice on a variety of Soils: with original Poetry. 8°,
pp. 39.
1,000 copies.

BUNGAY, G. W. Pen and Ink Portraits of the Senators, Assemblymen
and State Officers of the State of New York. 8°, pp. 84.
3,000 copies.

CATALOGUE of Books in the Library of the First Presbyterian Church
Sunday School. 18°, pp. 38.

CATALOGUE of Books in the Library of the Fourth Presbyterian Church
Sunday School, January, 1857. 18°, pp. 43.

CATALOGUE of Books in the North Pearl Street Baptist Sabbath School
Library. 18°, pp. 18.

CATALOGUE of Signor G. B. Pandolfini and Co.'s Great Auction Sale of
Marble, Agate and Alabaster Goods, Bohemian Glass and China Ware.
8°, pp. 10.

CATALOGUE of the Cohoes District School Library. 8°, pp. 29.
50 copies.

CATALOGUE of the Great Sale of the Mansion House Furniture, Broadway,
Albany, N. Y. 8°, pp. 22.

CATALOGUE of the Hudson Female Academy. 8°, pp. 24.
800 copies.

CASES in the Supreme Court of the State of New York.

CHARTER and Ordinances of the City of Omaha, Nebraska. 8°, pp. 74.
300 copies.

CHURCHILL'S Guide through the Albany Rural Cemetery : containing Illustrations of all the Principal Monuments, Tombs, &c. : the History of its Formation ; the Rules and Regulations for its Preservation, &c. &c. 12°, pp. 68, engravings. [4 copies, different editions.]
500 copies.

CIRCULAR and Catalogue of the Albany Female Academy, Founded A. D. 1814. Incorporated Feb. 16, 1821. 8°, pp. 20.
1,000 copies.

CONSTITUTION and By-Laws of Glenville Lodge No. 363, I. O. of O. F. of Northern New York. 18°, pp.

CONSTITUTION and By-Laws of Ocean Engine Company, No 3 of Greenbush. 18°, pp. 11.

CONSTITUTION and By-Laws of the Albany Young Men's Christian Association, founded February, 1857. 8°, pp. 18.
800 copies.

CONSTITUTION and By-Laws of the Young Men's Catholic Institute, attached to the Cathedral of the Immaculate Conception ; established with the approbation of the Rector, Dec., 1852. 12°, pp. 22.

CONSTITUTION, Rules and Regulations of Warren Engine Company, No. 12; adopted August, 1857. 18°, pp. 11.

CRUIKSHANK, JAMES. The New York Teacher: a Monthly Periodical, devoted to the Cause of General Education, and to the elevation of the Teachers' Profession. Vol, VI. from Oct., 1856 to Sept., 1857. 8°, pp. viii, 584.
4,500 copies.

CURTIS, NEWTON M. The Bride of the Northern Wilds, a tale of 1743. 8°, pp. 192.
1,200 copies.

DEBATES on the Trinity Church Bill, in the Senate of the State of New York. 8°, pp. 98.
1,000 copies.

DESCRIPTION of the Patent Distiller's Column, manufactured by P. H. Griffin, Copper Smith and Plumber, corner of James and Steuben Streets. 12°, pp. 12.

DOCTRINE of Divorce. 8°, pp. 37.

EIGHTH Annual Report of the Inspectors of the Albany Penitentiary. 8°, pp. 49.
1,200 copies.

EMMONS, EBENEZER. American Geology, containing a Statement of the Principles of the Science, with full Illustrations of the Characteristic American Fossils, with an Atlas and a Geological Map of the United States. 8°, part vi, pp. 152, plates.
960 copies. Vol. II and part v, or the first part of vol. III, were not printed.

EXERCISES of the Alumnæ of the Albany Female Academy, on their Sixteenth Anniversary, Thursday, June 25, 1857. 8°, pp. 72.
300 copies.

FINE, JOHN. An Address on the Character of the Apostle Paul, delivered before the Society of Enquiry of Princeton Theological Seminary, May, 1856. 8°, pp. 18.
100 copies.

[FINE, JOHN.] Lecture on the Resurrection of the Body : compiled from the Writings of Paul, Dick, Hall, and others , by a Layman. 8°, pp. 28.
100 copies. The author died Jan. 1867.

FIRST Annual Report of the Bible Society of Montgomery County, presented at Fort Plain, Sept., 1856, with Statistics. 8°, pp. 24.

FIRST Annual Report of the Managers of St. Paul's Church Home, for the year ending Dec. 31, 1856. 12°, pp. 12.

FLOATING Bethel moored in the Little Basin. 8°, pp. 4.

FORTY-SIXTH Annual Report of the Albany County Bible Society, organized A. D. 1810. 12°, pp. 16.

FOURTEENTH Annual Report of the Albany City Missionary Society, presented May, 1857. 12°, pp. 20.
400 copies.

GENERAL order and Act of April 15, 1857, for the adjustment of the New York Militia Claims of 1812. 8°, pp. 4.

[GOODSON, WILLIAM.] Poems by Eaglestone. 12°, pp. 104.
1,000 copies. Nearly all went to the paper mill, and the author died of consumption.

GOWANS, WM. Catalogue of Books on Political Economy, Banking, Theory of Government, Legislation, Jurisprudence, Political Philosophy, Slavery, Anti-Slavery, and Kindred Subjects, for sale at the affixed Prices, Store 81, 83 and 85 Centre Street, New York. 8°, pp. 40.

GRAVIER, Jacques. Relation de ce qui s'est passé dans la Mission de l'Immaculate Conception, au Pays des Ilinois, depuis de mois de Mars 1693, jusqu'au Fevrier 1694. 8°, pp. 66.
100 copies.

INDUSTRIAL School. Annual Report of the Children's Friend Society. 12°, pp. 12.

KIRCHENORDNUNG der Deutschen Evangelisch-Lutherischen Zion's-Kirche zu Boston, Mass., Ecke von Shawmut Avenue und Waltham Street, under der Aufsicht des Pastors A. Uebelacker. 12°, pp. 11.
500 copies.

KIRCHENORDNUNG der Evangelisch-Lutherischen Synode, das Staates New York, besonders abgedrukt fur die Gemeinden der Pastors Daniel Stahlschmidt, namlich fur die Evangelisch-Lutherischen St. Paul's Gemeinde zu Liverpool, Onondaga Co., N. Y. und fur die Ev. Luth. St. Paul's Gemeinde zu Oswego, N. Y. 12°, pp. 7.

LALOR, T. M. Reports of Cases argued and determined in the late Supreme Court of the State of New York. 8°, pp. 489.

LAWS and By-Laws of the Medical Society of the State of New York, with the Rules of Order, Medical Ethics, &c.; prepared for the use of the Society at its Annual Meetings. 8°, pp. 40.
1,000 copies.

McCoy & Clark, Stove Manufacturers, Office Nos. 13 and 15 Green Street, Foundery, Montgomery Street, Albany, N. Y. 8°, pp. 41.

McELROY, THOMAS. Review of the Water Commissioners' Report for 1856. 8°, pp. 35.
500 copies.

MEMBERS of Master's Lodge of Free and Accepted Masons, City of Albany, State of New York. Date of Warrant as No 2, granted by the Grand Lodge of England, 5th day of March, 1768; date of Warrant as No 2, granted by the Grand Lodge of the State of New York, 4th day of April, 1798; renumbered to hail as No 5, 7th day of June, 1839. 16°, pp. 16.

MINUTES of the Particular Synod of Albany convened in Regular Session in the 1st Reformed Dutch Church of Schenectady, May 2, 1855. 8°, pp. 16.
700 copies.

MINUTES of the Seventeenth Anniversary of the Rensselaerville Association, held in the Meeting House of the Baptist Church in Rensselaerville, commencing Sept. 11, 1857. 8°, pp. 16.
700 copies.

MINUTES of the Sixty-second Synod of the Evangelical Lutheran Ministerium of the State of New York, and Adjacent States and Countries, held at Zion's German Evan. Luth. Church, Utica, N. Y., Sept. 5 to Sept. 9, 1857. 8°, pp. 48.
500 copies.

MINUTES of the Twenty-seventh Convention of the Hartwick Synod of the Evangelical Lutheran Church in the State of New York, held at Athens, Greene county, N. Y., Sept. 12–26, 1857. 8°, pp. 32.
1,000 copies.

MUNSELL, JOEL. Annals of Albany, vol. VIII. 12°, pp. 376.
350 copies.

MUNSELL, JOEL. Catalogue of American and Foreign Books, in Bibliography and other Departments of Literature, offered at the low prices affixed, by J. Munsell, 78 State Street, Albany, N. Y., consisting of Rare Works relating to Printing, Voyages and Travels, Dictionaries, Biographies, and Periodicals, Antiquities, Languages, Local History, &c. 8°, pp. 74.

MUNSELL, J. Webster's Calendar or the Albany Almanac, for the year of our Lord 1858. 12°, pp. 36.

NOTT, BENJAMIN. Constitutional Ethics. Nos. 1 and 2. 8°, pp. 20, 23.
300 copies.

[O'CALLAGHAN, E. B.] Commissary Wilson's Orderly Book; Expedition of the British and Provincial Army, under Maj. Gen. Jeffery Amherst, against Ticonderoga and Crown Point, 1759. 4°, pp. xi, 220.
100 copies. Notes by Dr. E. B. O'Callaghan.

OFFICIAL Proceedings of the American State Council, held at Troy, N. Y. Feb. 24 and 25, 1857, with the Platform, Resolutions and Address. 18°, pp. 14.
8,000 copies.

PALMER, RAY. Address on the Ministry of the Future, delivered in the Tremont Temple, Boston, at the Anniversary of the Congregational Library Association, May 26, 1857. 8°, pp. 32.

PATTERN List of Townsend's Furnace and Machine Shop, Albany, N. Y., comprising a Catalogue of the Wheel and Pully Patterns, and Racks and Roll Chills, attached to that Establishment. 4th Edition. 8°, xvi, 26. Supplement to the above, pp. 12.
2,000 copies.

PRAYERS for Passion Week. 12°, pp. 8.

PRAYER Meetings. 12°, pp. 12.

PROCEEDINGS of the Convention of the Soldiers of the War of 1812, in the State of New York, held at Schuylerville, Saratoga County, Oct.. 17, 1856, in reference to their claims for Military Services, and to celebrate the Anniversary of Burgoyne's Surrender. 8°, pp. 34.
1,000 copies.

PROCEEDINGS of the Board of Supervisors of the County of Otsego for the year 1856. 8°, pp. 29.
2,000 copies.

QUACKENBUSH, JOHN V. P. An Address delivered before the Students of the Albany Medical College, introductory to the Course on Obstetrics, April 14, 1857. 8°, pp. 16.

RAPLER, Rob. [Dr. O. C. Alexander.] The Hermit of Aleova : or the Shepherd Girl's Triumphs. 12°, pp. 380.
200 copies.

REMARKS of Hon. Thomas G. Alvord, before the Special Committee, to whom was referred the Petitions for a Pro Rata Freight Law. 8°, pp. 8.

REPORT of the Forty-fourth Annual Examination of the Albany Female Academy, and of the Exercises of the Alumnæ of the Institution, June 26, 1857. 8°, pp. 22.
500 copies.

ROGERS, E. P. The Sovereignty of God in Calamity : a Discourse delivered in the North Dutch Church in Albany, Sept. 20, 1857, being the Sabbath after the Intelligence was received of the Loss of the Central America. 8°, pp. 28.
300 copies.

SCHMIDT, HENRY J. Congregational Singing ; a Report presented to the Evangelical Lutheran Ministerium of the State of New York, at their Sixty-second Synodical Session, Utica, N. Y., Sept. 8, 1857. 8°, pp. 8.

SEVENTH Annual Report of the Troy Conference Missionary Society ; auxiliary to the Missionary Society of the Methodist Episcopal Church, 1857. 12°, pp. 36.
5,000 copies.

SIMMS, J. R. The American Spy, or Freedom's Early Sacrifice : a Tale of the Revolution, founded upon Fact. 8°, pp. 63.
1,000 copies.

SIXTH and Seventh Annual Catalogue of the Hudson Female Academy, Hudson, N. Y. 8°, pp. 24.

[SKERRITT, Miss.] Catalogue and Circular of the Young Ladies' Institute No. 4 High Street, nearly opposite the Capitol, Albany, N. Y. Founded 1842. 8°, pp.

SPEECH of Mr. Wadsworth in the Senate of New York in the Matter of Trinity Church, March 27, 1857. 8°, pp. 10.
1,750 copies.

To the Members of the Duanesburgh Quarterly Meeting. 8°, pp. 3.

TRINITY CHURCH. Argument of Hon. Daniel E. Sickles in the Senate of the State of New York, April, 1857, on the Trinity Church Bill. 8°, pp. 85.
3,000 copies.

TWENTY-FIRST Annual Report of the Albany City Tract and Missionary Society presented at the Annual Meeting in the Congregational Church, Dec. 21, 1856 ; incorporated January, 1856. 8°, pp. 26.
1,200 copies.

TWENTY-SIXTH Anniversary of the Stephentown Baptist Association held in the meeting house of the Baptist Church in Berlin, Sept. 9 and 10, 1857. 8°, pp. 12.
400 copies.

VERHANDLUNGEN der Zwei und sechzigsten Synode des Evangel. Lutherischen Ministeriums der Staates New York und angrenzender Staaten und Lander. Gehalten in der Deutschen Evang. Lutherischen Zion's Kirche zu Utica, N. Y. Beginnend Sonnabend, den 5 Sept. und endend Mittwoch, den 9 Sept., 1857. 8°, pp. 40.
500 copies.

WILLARD, SYLVESTER D. Biographical Memoirs of Physicians of Albany
County; an Address delivered before the Medical Society of the County
of Albany, at its Semi-Annual Meeting, June 9, 1857. 8°, pp. 24.
  300 copies.

WILLARD, SYLVESTER D. Eulogy upon the Life and Character of Hiram
Augustus Edmonds, M.D., Superintendent of the Lydius Street Mission
Sabbath School, delivered before the Teachers and Friends of the Mis-
sion, on Wednesday Evening, April 29, 1857. 8°, pp. 20.

WYCKOFF, J. N. John, Surnamed Boanerges; A Discourse in Memory
of Rev. John Ludlow, D.D., LL.D., delivered in the Pulpit of the Ref.
Prot. Dutch Church of Albany, Oct. 4, 1857. 8°, pp. 32.
  600 copies.

1858.

ACT of Incorporation and Constitution and By-Laws of the Albany Benevolent Association of Segar Makers; organized 1844; incorporated March
7, 1857. 18°, pp. 18.
  100 copies.

ADAMS, SAMPSON & Co. The Albany Directory for the year 1858; containing a General Directory of the Citizens, a Business Directory, and
other Miscellaneous Matter. 8°, pp. 224.
  1,600 copies.

ALBANY and Susquehanna Rail Road, its probable Cost and Revenue,
being Remarks submitted to Richard Franchot, Esq., President of the
Company, by C. W. Wents, Chief Engineer, and ordered printed for
the Information of the Stockholders. 8°, pp. 18.
  200 copies.

ALLEN, R. L., M.D. An Analysis of the Principal Mineral Fountains at
Saratoga Springs, embracing an Account of their History; their Chemi-
cal and Curative Properties; together with General Directions for their
Use; Also some Remarks upon the Natural History, and Objects of
General Interest in the County of Saratoga. 16°, pp. 114.
  1,300 copies.

AMSTERDAM Bridge Question. 8°, pp. 7.

ANNUAL Catalogue of the Officers and Students of Hartwick Theological
and Classical Seminary for the academic year ending Aug. 25, 1858,
8°, pp. 12.

ANNUAL Catalogue of the Officers and Students of the Sand Lake Collegiate Institute, Sand Lake, N. Y. 4 Catalogues, 16 pp. each, 8°.

ANNUAL Exercises of Mrs. Loveridge's School. 8°, pp. 12.
  400 copies.

ANNUAL Report of the Board of Education of the City of Albany, to the Common Council, for the year ending June 1, 1858. 8°, pp. 31.

ANNUAL Report of the Industrial School. 8°, pp. 12.
500 copies.

ARTICLES of Association and By-Laws of the Knox Mutual Insurance Association. 12°, pp. 12.

ARTICLES of Faith and Covenant adopted by the First Congregational Church in Middlefield, March 12, 1858. 32°, pp. 8.

BENEDICT, ERASTUS C. An Address delivered at the Closing Exercises of the Twenty-eighth Term of the New York State Normal School, July 8, 1858. 8°, pp. 21.

BIGOT, JACQUE. Relation de ce qvi s'est passé de plus remarqvable dans la Mission Abnaquise de Sainct Joseph de Sillery et de Sainct Francois de Sales, l'anneé 1685. 8°, pp. 21.
110 copies.

BIGOT, VINCENT. Relation de ce qvi s'est passé de plvs remarqvable dans la Mission des Abnaquise à L'Acadie, l'anneé 1701. 8°, pp. 34.
210 copies.

BILL of Timber and Joists for the New York State Agricultural College ; S. E. Hewes, Architect, 55 State Street, Albany. 12, pp. 12.

BOUTON, J. W. & Co. Catalogue of Books. Square 8°, pp. 20.
2,000 copies.

BOUTON, J. W. & Co. Catalogue of Books. Square 8°, pp. 24.
2,000 copies.

BURNHAM, LOUIS W. Book keeping, its Rules and Reasons. 8°, pp. 16.

BY-LAWS of the Albany and Rensselaer Counties Cricket Club; together with the Laws of Cricket, as revised by the Marylebone Cricket Club. 32°, pp. 20.

BY-LAWS of the Board of Education and Acts relating to the Public Schools in the City of Albany. 8°, pp. 32.
250 copies.

BY-LAWS, Rules and Regulations of Columbia Lodge No. 98, of Free and Accepted Masons, Chatham Four Corners, N. Y., adopted Nov. 20, 1858. 32°, pp. 26.

CASES in the Court of Appeals of the State of New York. 8°.
20 copies.

CASES in the Supreme Court of the State of New York. 8°.
12 copies.

CATALOGUE of Hartwick Seminary. 8°, pp.
300 copies.

CATALOGUE of Law Blanks published and for Sale by Fisk & Little, Booksellers, Stationers and Blank Book Manufacturers. 12°, pp. 8.

CATALOGUE of Oil Paintings. 8°, pp. 8.

CATALOGUE of the Arbor Hill Methodist Episcopal Church Sabbath School
Library. 16°, pp. 16.
200 copies.

CATALOGUE of the Officers and Students of the Rensselaerville Academy,
for the Academic year 1857-8. 8°, pp. 12.

CATALOGUE of the Saratoga Female Seminary, at Temple Grove, Saratoga
Springs, N. Y. 8°, pp. 20.
1,000 copies.

CATALOGUE of the Scholars' Library of the Sabbath School Association,
connected with the First Baptist Church of Albany ; organized May 16,
1858. 16°, pp. 16.

CAVELIER, M. Relation du Voyage enterpris par feu M. Robert Cavelier,
Sieur de la Salle, pour decouvrir dans le golfe du Mexique l'embouchure
du Fleuve de Mississipy. 8°, pp. 54.
110 copies, and 6 on large paper.

CHAUMONOT. La Vie du R. P. Pierre Joseph Marie Chaumonot, de la
Compagnie de Jesus, Missionaire dans la Nouvelle France, Ecrite par
lui–même par ordre de son Supériéur, l'an 1688. Small 4°, pp. 108.

CHURCHILL, HENRY W. Illustrated Guide to the Albany Rural Cemetery.
12°, pp. 20.
250 copies.

CIRCULAR and Catalogue of the Albany Female Academy, Founded A. D.
1814. Incorporated February 16, 1821. 8°, pp. 20.

COAST Survey : its Cost, Abuses and Power. 8°, pp. 15.
5,000 copies 1st edition; 2,000 copies 2d edition.

CONCERT Hymns. 8°, pp. 8.

CONFESSION of Faith and Covenants of the Fourth Presbyterian Church,
Albany, N. Y. 16°, pp. 12.
300 copies.

CONSTITUTION and By-Laws of Yellow Jacket Hose Company No. VIII,
organized Aug. 1st, 1857. 16°, pp. 16.
300 copies.

CONSTITUTION, By-Laws and Rules of Order of Farmers and Mechanics'
Lodge No. 157, I. O. of O. F. under the Jurisdiction of the Grand Lodge
of Northern New York, located at Greenbush, Rens. Co., N. Y. 16°,
pp. 32.

CONSTITUTION of the Hartwick Synod. 8°, pp. 24.
300 copies.

CONSTITUTION of the Young Men's Christian Association of Waterford,
N. Y., organized April 28, 1858. 8°, pp. 14.
200 copies.

CONVERSATIONS with a Churchman upon Religious Matters ; a Tract for
our own Neighborhood, with Notes, by the Rector of Trinity Church,
in the County [of Albany]. 12°, pp. 44.

DUDLEY Observatory; Speeches of John N. Wilder and Thomas W. Olcott, June, 1858, before the Trustees, with Resolutions of the Board. 8°, pp. 28.
500 copies.

DURRIE, DANIEL S. Steele Family; a Genealogical History of John and George Steele, Settlers of Hartford, Conn., 1835-6, and their Descendants; with an appendix containing Genealogical Information respecting other Families of the Name who settled in different Parts of the United States. Royal 8°, pp. 154.   *see 1859*
300 copies.

EXERCISES of the Alumnæ of the Albany Female Academy, on their Seventeenth Anniversary, Tuesday, June 22, 1858. 8°, pp. 81.
400 copies.

FIFTEENTH Annual Report of the Albany City Missionary Society, presented May, 1858. 12°, pp. 15.
400 copies.

FIRST Annual Report of the Albany Young Men's Christian Association, presented March 22, 1858, with the By-Laws, List of Officers, Members, etc., etc. 8°, pp. 42.
1,000 copies.

FORTY-SEVENTH Annual Report of the Albany County Bible Society, organized A. D. 1810. 12°, pp. 15.
1,000 copies.

GILBERT, JOHN P. A Treatise on Deafness and Diseases of the Eye and Ear, with Remarks on their Nature and Cure; illustrated with Cases. 8°, pp. 11.

GOWANS, WM. Catalogue of Books. 8°, pp. 40.
4,000 copies.

GUILD, REUBEN A. The Librarian's Manual; a Treatise on Bibliography, comprising a Select and Descriptive List of Bibliographical Works; to which are added, Sketches of Publick Libraries, Illustrated with Engravings. By Reuben A. Guild, A.M., Librarian of Brown University, Providence, R. I. Cap 4°, pp. 10, 304.
500 copies.

HICKCOX, JOHN H. An Historical Account of American Coinage. 8°, pp. 151.
250 copies.

HOUGH, F. B. Proclamations for Thanksgiving, issued by the Continental Congress, President Washington, by the National and State Governments on the Peace of 1815, and by the Governors of New York since the Introduction of the Custom; with those of the Governors of the several States in 1858; with an Historical Introduction and Notes. Royal 8°, pp. xvii, 183.
200 copies.

JOHNSON, GEORGE Y. American Nationality; the Sovereignty of the People; Speech of Hon. George Y. Johnson, of the Thirteenth District, delivered in the Senate of New York, March 11, 1858, on the Kansas Resolutions offered by Hon. O. B. Wheeler, as a Substitute for the Resolutions of Mr. Diven. 8°, pp. 7.
2,600 copies.

JOURNAL of the Proceedings of the National Teachers' Association, at the First Anniversary, held in Cincinnati, O., Aug. 11, 1858, with the Constitution and Lectures. 8°, pp. 62.

KENNEDY, DUNCAN. A Clergyman's Idea of a Model Physician; an Address delivered at the Commencement of the Albany Medical College June 8, 1858. 8°, pp. 24.
500 copies.

KEYES, EMERSON W. The Educational System of the State of New York; An Address delivered before the New York State Teachers' Association at Lockport, Aug. 5, 1858. 8°, pp 19.

LAWS of the State of New York, passed at the Eighty-first Session of the Legislature, begun January fifth, and ended April nineteenth, 1858, in the city of Albany. 8°, pp. 783.
5,000 copies.

LOUNSBERRY, B. Catalogue and Circular of the Rensselaerville Academy. 8°, pp.
200 copies.

LETTERS to Benjamin Franklin from his Family and Friends, 1751–1790. 8°, pp. 195.
250 copies, and 10 large paper. Portraits of Mrs. Franklin and Mrs. Bache.

LOWRY, ROBERT. The Power of Faith; a Discourse delivered on the Sunday after Trinity, A. D. 1858, being the Fifth Anniversary of the Organization of the Church of the Messiah, Greenbush, N. Y. 8°, pp. 13

MABEY, JEROME A. What is Homœopathy? Its Positions defined and contrasted with Allopathy; a Lecture before Literary and Scientific. Societies. 8°, pp. 31.
500 copies.

MEDICINE of the Age: Gibson's Syrup for Scrofula, and all Diseases of the Blood. 16°, pp. 16.

MEEK and HAYDEN. Descriptions of New Organic Remains from Northeastern Kansas, indicating the Existence of Permian Rocks in that Territory. 8°, pp. 16.
100 copies.

MILLER, SAMUEL. The Bishop and the Bible, or the Nail Driven Home: by a Layman: also Outlines of a Sermon on Woman's Rights; or Vice Versa, the Rights of Women in all Ages, Stages and Nations. 12°, pp. 35.
100 copies.

MINUTES of the Evangelical Lutheran Ministerium of the State of New
York. 8°, pp. 48.
500 copies.

MINUTES of the Fifty-fifth Anniversary of the Synod of Albany, convened
at Salem, Oct. 12, 1858 (with an appendix). 8°, pp. 36.

MINUTES of the Particular Synod of Albany. 8°, pp.
300 copies.

MINUTES of the Synod of Albany. 8°, pp 20.
1,200 copies.

MUNICIPAL Independence ; the Right of the People to govern themselves ;
Speech of Hon. James H. Lynch of New York, in the Assembly of the
State of New York, Friday, March 12, 1858, on the Bill to repeal the
Metropolitan Police Law. 8°, pp. 15.
2,000 copies.

MUNSELL, JOEL.   Annals of Albany, Vol. IX.   12°, pp. 389.

MUNSELL, JOEL.   Catalogue of Books. 8°, pp. 40.
300 copies.

MUNSELL, JOEL.   The Every Day Book of History and Chronology. 8°,
pp. 536.
1,000 copies.

MUNSELL, JOEL.   Webster's Calendar, or the Albany Almanac for the year
of our Lord 1859.   12°, pp. 36.

MURPHY, W. D.   Biographical Sketches of Members of the Legislature.
12°, pp. 144.
3,000 copies ; 250 copies on fine paper.

NEBRASKA.   The Criminal Code of Nebraska. 8°, pp. 76.

NINTH Annual Catalogue of the Spencertown Academy, Spencertown,
N. Y. 8°, pp. 12.

NINTH Annual Report of the Inspectors of the Albany Penitentiary. 8°,
pp. 39.
1,200 copies.

NO More Debt; No Increase of Taxation ; Application of unclaimed
Dividends and Deposits to the completion of the Canals ; Speech of
Hon. S. A. Law, delivered in the House of Assembly, April 5th, 1858.
8°, pp. 9.
3,000 copies.

OPINION on the Constitutional Power of the Legislature to repeal the
Second Section of the Act of January 25, 1814, entitled An Act to Alter
the name of the corporation of Trinity Church in New York, and for
other purposes. 8°, pp. 13.
100 copies.

PROCEEDINGS and Catalogue of the Washington County Teachers' Institute, held at Cambridge, commencing Nov. 2, 1857. 8°, pp. 12.

PROCEEDINGS of the Military Association of the State of New York at the Special Meeting in Albany, Jan., 1858. 8°, pp. 40.
600 copies.

PROCEEDINGS of the National Teachers' Association. 8°, pp. 62.
100 copies.

PROCEEDINGS of the Tanners' Convention, held at the Oquaga House, in Deposit, N. Y., Tuesday afternoon, April 27, 1858. 8°, pp. 36.

POINTS in the Court of Appeals of the State of New York. 8°.
20 copies.

RAIL ROAD Influences: Speech of Hon. A. H. Laflin, of the Twentieth District (Otsego and Herkimer), delivered in the Senate, Tuesday, March 2d, 1858. 8°, pp. 7.

RATHBONE & Co. Stove Books. 8°, pp. 56.
3,000 copies.

REMARKS, &c. Albany and Susquehanna Rail Road Company. 8°, pp. 18.
1,000 copies.

REPORT of the Forty-fifth Annual Examination of the Albany Female Academy ; and of the Exercises of the Alumnæ of the Institution, on their seventeenth Anniversary, June 22, 1856. 8°, pp. 19.
1,000 copies.

REPORTS of the President and Treasurer of the Albany Young Men's Christian Association, presented at the Annual Meeting, held at the Second Presbyterian Church, on Monday Evening, March 22, 1858. 12°, pp. 12.

REPORTS of the Third Annual Examination of Mrs. Loveridge's School, and the Commencement Exercises on their Third (&c.) Anniversary. 8°.

REVIVAL of Religion ; a Discourse, preached in the Division Street Chapel, Sabbath Evening, March 21, 1858, by Rev. A. D. Mayo. 8°, pp. 8.

REYNOLDS, DEXTER. Report of an Investigation into the Manufacture of Paper from Wood, at the Mill of the Ligneous Paper Company, Little Falls, N. Y. 8°, pp. 24.
50 copies.

RICE, E. B. Exercises for teaching Book-keeping by Double Entry, Book C. Oblong 8°, pp. 8.

ROGERS, E. P. A Historical Discourse on the Reformed Protestant Dutch Church of Albany, delivered on Thanksgiving day, Nov. 26, 1857, in the North Dutch Church. 8°, pp. 120.
1,000 copies.

SECOND Annual Report of the Bible Society of Montgomery County, presented at St. Johnsville, Sept. 1857, with Statistics. 8°, pp. 28.

SECOND Annual Report of the Directors of the Mutual Insurance Association of Nassau, Schodack and Chatham. 12°, pp. 12.

SIXTH and Seventh Annual Catalogue of the Hudson Female Academy, Hudson, N. Y.   8°, pp. 24.

SPECIFICATIONS, Materials and Labor to be employed in the Building for the New York State Agricultural College, to be erected in the town of Ovid, Seneca Co., New York; S. E. Hewes, Architect, 55 State Street, Albany.   12°, pp. 20.
50 copies.

THIRD Annual Report of the Windham School Visitors, to the Electors of said Town, Oct. 4, 1858.   8°, pp. 14.

TWENTY-SECOND Anuual Report of the Albany City Tract and Missionary Society, presented at the Annual Meeting in the Middle Dutch Church, December 20, 1857. 8°, pp. 28.
1,200 copies.

VERHANDLUNGEN.   8°, pp. 52.
500 copies.

WHO withholds Cooperation ?   Correspondence between the Officers of the Board of Trustees of the Dudley Observatory and the Directors of the same Institution.   8°, pp. 53.
500 copies.

WRITINGS of Wm. Law.   12°, pp.
1,000 copies.   For F. S. Pease.

WYCKOFF, I. N.   She is not Dead but Sleepeth: a Sermon preached in the Second Reformed Protestant Dutch Church, Albany, N. Y., Sunday, Oct. 3, 1858.   8°, pp. 25.
400 copies.

WYCKOFF, I. N, The Spiritual Portrait: A Funeral Sermon on the Death of the Hon. Jacob Lansing, Jr., delivered in the Middle Dutch Church, Albany, March 28, 1858.   8°, pp. 40.

1859.

ADAMS, SAMPSON & Co.   The Albany Directory for the year 1859; containing a General Directory of the Citizens, a Business Directory, and other Miscellaneous Matter.   8°, pp. 235.
1,400 copies.

ADAMS, SAMPSON & Co.   Troy Directory.   12°, pp. 418.
800 copies.

ALBANY and Susquehanna Rail Road, its probable Cost and Revenue, being Remarks submitted to Richard Franchot, Esq., President of the Company, by C. W. Wentz, Chief Engineer, and ordered printed for the information of the Stockholders; to which is appended a List of Directors and Officers, and the Report of the President to the Board of Directors, made at the last Annual Meeting.   8°, pp. 24.
400 copies.

AMERICAN Institute of Homœopathy; Festivities at Boston; the Dinner and Levee at Faneuil Hall, June 2, 1859. 8°, pp. 19.

ANNUAL Catalogue of the Officers and Students of Hartwick Theological and Classical Seminary, for the Academic year ending Aug. 24, 1859. 8°, pp. 12.

ANNUAL Catalogue of the Officers and Students of the Sand Lake Collegiate Institute, Sand Lake, N. Y. 8°. 16 pp.

BIENNIAL Report of the Lutheran Foreign Missionary Society. 8°, pp. 16.
500 copies.

BOUTON, J. W. & Co. Catalogue of Books. Square 8°, pp. 36.
1,500 copies.

BROADWAY Mission Sunday School, auxiliary to the Albany Methodist Sunday School Union; organized 25th of June, 1854. 16°, pp. 32.

BY-LAWS of Ancient City Lodge, No. 452, of the Most Ancient and Honorable Fraternity of Free and Accepted Masons; together with extracts from the Constitution of the W. G. L. of the State of New York. 16°, pp. 24.

BY-LAWS of Knickerbocker Lodge No. 76, I. O. S. M. 16°, pp. 20.

BY-LAWS of Wadsworth Lodge No. 417, of Free and Accepted Masons of the State of New York; instituted Jan. 23, A.L. 5856; chartered June 12, 5857. 16°, pp. 52.

CASES in the Court of Appeals in the State of New York. 8°.
20 copies.

CASES in the Supreme Court of the State of New York. 8°.
12 copies.

CASE in the Supreme Court of the State of New York, Judiah Ellsworth against Lewis Curtis, et al. 8°, pp. 574.
25 copies. This case was printed in four days as far as it went, but was never completed, nor any portion of it paid for.

CATALOGUE of Books in the Library of the First Presbyterian Church Sunday School. 18°, pp. 20.

CATALOGUE of Books in the North Pearl Street Baptist Sabbath School Library. 16°, pp. 16.

CATALOGUE of Books in the Sabbath School of the Third Reformed Dutch Church, Cor. of Ferry and Green Streets, in the City of Albany. 18°, pp 26.

CATALOGUE of Books in the Sunday School Library of the Methodist Episcopal Church, Ferry Street, Albany. 16°, pp. 16.
2 copies.

CATALOGUE of Law Blanks published by Banks & Brothers, Law Publishers, 475 Broadway, Albany, 1859. 16°, pp. 16.

CATALOGUE of the Albany Medical College. 8°, pp. 8.
5,000 copies.

CATALOGUE of the Law School of the University of Albany. 8°, pp. 16.
1,500 copies.

CATALOGUE of the Library of the Troy Young Men's Association. 8°, pp.
iv, 232.

CATALOGUE of the Sunday School Library of the Garretson Station M.-E.
Church. 16°, pp. 16.

CIRCULAR and Catalogue of the Albany Female Academy. Founded
A. D. 1814, Incorporated Feb. 16, 1821. 8°, pp. 22.
1,000 copies.

COAST Survey: Reply to the Official Defence of its Cost, Abuses and
Power. 8°, pp. 36.
6,000 copies.

COLE, HIRAM. Washington County Business Directory. 18°, pp. 108.
1,500 copies.

COLTON, A. The Dental Mirror. 8°, pp. 24.

COLVIN & BINGHAM. Review of the Manor Question. 8°, pp. 87.

CONSTITUTION and By-Laws of St. Mary's Library Association, organized
March 14, 1849; rooms No. 43 Chapel Street. 16°, pp. 16.

CONSTITUTION and By-Laws of the Albany Medical Association, instituted
January 6, 1859. 8°, pp. 8.

CONSTITUTION and By-Laws of the Union Musical Association of Albany,
N. Y.; organized Oct. 11th, 1858. 18°, pp. 14.

COUNCIL Journal of the Legislative Assembly of the Territory of Nebraska,
Fifth Session, begun and held at Omaha City, Sept. 21, A. D. 1858.
8°, pp. 292.
1,000 copies.

CRUIKSHANK, JAMES. The New York Teacher; a Monthly Periodical,
devoted to the Cause of General Education, and to the Elevation of the
Teachers' Profession. Vol. VIII. 8°, pp. iv, 570.
2,800 copies.

CRUIKSHANK, JAMES. The New York Teacher: a Monthly Periodical,
devoted to the Cause of General Education, and to the Elevation of the
Teachers' Profession. Vol. IX. 8°, pp. iv, 568.
2,800 copies.

DURRIE, DANIEL STEELE. Steele Family; a Genealogical History of
John and George Steele (settlers at Hartford, Conn.), 1635–6, and their
Descendants. With an Appendix, containing genealogical information
respecting other families of the name who settled in other parts of the
United States. Royal 8°, pp. x, 145.
300 copies.

EXERCISES of the Alumnæ of the Albany Female Academy, on their
Eighteenth Anniversary, Tuesday, June 21, 1859. 8°, pp. 38.
300 copies.

FORTY-EIGHTH Annual Report of the Albany County Bible Society, organized A. D. 1810. 12°, pp. 15.

GILBERT, JOHN P. A Treatise on Deafness and Diseases of the Eye and Ear, with Remarks on their Nature and Cure; illustrated with Cases. 8°, pp.

GOWANS. Catalogue of Standard Books, for Sale at the affixed Prices, Store 81, 83 and 85 Centre Street, New York. 8°, pp. 28.
12 pages Addenda not printed by me.

[HOUGH, F. B.] Life of Te-ho-ra-gwa-ne-gen, alias Thomas Williams, a Chief of the Caughnawaga Tribe of Indians in Canada; by Rev. Eleazer Williams, reputed son of Thomas Williams, and by many believed to be Louis XVII, son of the last reigning monarch of France previous to the Revolution of 1789. 8°, pp. 91.
200 copies.

HOUGH, F. B. Papers concerning the Attack on Hatfield and Deerfield, by a Party of Indians from Canada, Sept. 19th, 1677. 8°, pp. 82.
100 copies. This was the first of the series of Books issued by the Bradford Club. It has sold as high as $50, in paper covers.

HOUSE Journal of the Legislative Assembly of the Territory of Nebraska, fifth Session, began and held at Omaha City, Sept. 21, A. D. 1858. 8°, pp. 274.
1,000 copies.

JAMES Estate. In the Supreme Court of the State of New York; Augustus James, Plaintiff, against William James, et al., Defendants; Complaint in Partition. 8°, pp. 109.
100 copies.

LAWS, Joint Resolutions and Memorials passed at the Fifth Session of the Legislative Assembly of the Territory of Nebraska, begun at Omaha City, N. T., Sept. 21, 1858, together with the Constitution of the United States and the Organic Law. 8°, pp. 455.
1,500 copies.

LOWVILLE Academy Semi-Centennial Anniversary, celebrated at Lowville, N. Y., July 21st and 22d, 1858. 8°, pp. 133.
1,000 copies. Portraits.

MANUAL of the Congregational Church, Greenwich. 12°, pp. 32.
500 copies.

MATTHEW GRANT's Old Church Record. 8°, pp. 14.
50 copies.

MEMORIALS of Mrs. John V. L. Pruyn. 4°, pp. 77.
131 copies. Portraits and plates.

MINUTES of the Common Council. 8°, pp. 636.

MINUTES of the Particular Synod of Albany. 8°, pp. 35.
300 copies.

MINUTES of the Sixty-Third Anniversary of the Rensselaerville Association, held in the Meeting House of the Baptist Church at Sloansville, Schoharie County, N. Y., commencing Wednesday, Sept. 21, 1859. 8°, pp. 16.

MUNSELL, JOEL. Annals of Albany. Vol. X. 12°, pp. 501.
350 copies.

MUNSELL, JOEL. Webster's Calendar, or the Albany Almanac for the year of our Lord 1860. 12°, pp. 36.

MUNSELL'S Guide to the Hudson River by Rail Road and Steam Boat, with a colored Map. 16°, pp. 58.
2,000 copies. This was got up by Dr. Franklin B. Hough.

OLD JIM AVERY'S own Farrier and Recipe Book, being a cheaper, safer, and surer Method of Farriery than any ever before offered to the World : also disclosing the whole Secret and great Mystery, both ancient and modern, of Training and Educating the Horse, together with Hints on Breeding and Surgery; containing over one hundred choice Recipes for the prevention and cure of Diseases in Horses, illustrated with Engravings, etc., etc.; to which is prefixed a Biography of the Author, by a Friend, with a Life-like Portrait of Old Jim himself. 12°, pp. 340.
1,000 copies.

ORDERLY Book of the Northern Army, at Ticonderoga and Mt. Independence, from Oct. 17th, 1776 to Jan. 8th, 1777, with Biographical and Explanatory Notes, and an Appendix. 4°, pp. viii, 224.
130 copies small ; 10 large paper. Portrait and map.

PAINE, H. D. Diphtheria. Read before the Sixteenth Annual Meeting of the American Institute of Homœopathy, held in Boston, Mass., June 1, 1869. 8°, pp. 13.

PHILES, GEORGE P. Catalogue of Curious and Scarce Old Books in Various Languages and Departments of Literature, embracing a portion of a choice and valuable stock of Books recently imported from England, France, Germany and Holland, now for sale by Mauran & Philes, 55 Cedar St., New York. 8°, pp. 58.
1,000 copies.

POINTS in the Court of Appeals of the State of New York. 8°.
20 copies.

POINTS in the Supreme Court of the State of New York. 8°.
12 copies.

PROCEEDINGS of the Military Association of the State of New York at the Annual Meeting in Albany, Jan., 1859. 8°, pp. 109.
500 copies.

[RAWSON, T. R.] Sixteenth Annual Report of the Albany City Missionary Society, presented May 6, 1859. 12°, pp. 12.

REED, SYLVANUS. The Church, a House of Prayer for all; a Sermon preached on the Ninth Anniversary of the Opening of the Church of the Holy Innocents, Albany, Feb. 6, 1859. 8°, pp. 17.
500 copies.

REGISTERS des Baptesmes et Sepultures què sont Faits au Fort Duquesne pendant les années 1753, 1754, 1755, and 1756. Small 8°, pp 52.
120 copies; 10 large paper.

REPORT of the Forty-sixth Annual Examination of the Albany Female Academy; and of the Exercises of the Alumnæ of the Institution, on their Eighteenth Anniversary June 21, 1859. 8°, pp. 19.

ROGERS, E. P. The Strong Staff Broken; a Discourse in Memory of Hon. Teunis Van Vechten, pronounced Sunday, Feb. 13, 1859. 8°, pp. 38.
200 copies.

ROLLO, E. M. Arnold, a Model Teacher: an Address delivered before the New York State Teachers' Association, held at Poughkeepsie, Aug. 3, 1859. 8°, pp. 15.

[SILL, GEORGE G.] Genealogy of the Descendants of John Sill, who settled at Cambridge, Mass., in 1637. 12°, pp. 108.
200 copies. The author had gathered nearly all the facts he needed for his book, and wrote to his brother in Lyme, Conn., for the last information. The brother not responding, he wrote again. The reply came that he did not know anything about the matters, and if he did, of what consequence was it? This so horrified the author that he made the journey to gather the facts, and having done so, was there stricken with apoplexy and died.

SIXTEENTH Annual Report of the Albany City Missionary Society, presented May 6, 1859. 12°, pp. 12.
300 copies.

[SKERRIT, MISS.] Catalogue and Circular of the Young Ladies' Institute, No. 4 High Street, nearly opposite the Capitol, Albany, N. Y. Founded 1842. 8°, pp.

SMITH, WILLIAM R. The Jurisdiction of the Justices of the Peace, in Civil and Criminal Cases; and the Office and Duties of Judges of Probate; with Explanations and Forms for the use of Executors, Administrators and Guardians, and the Commissioners of Roads and Revenue; to which is added the Duties of every Subordinate Civil Officer in Commission in the State of Alabama; all arranged under the Law as now in force; with an appendix, containing numerous Forms for Conveyances, and the School Law. 8°, pp. 558.
2,000 copies.

SPICER, TOBIAS. Spirit Life. 12°, pp. 216.
500 copies.

SPRAGUE, W. B. Memoir of Mrs. John V. L. Pruyn. 8°, pp. 29.
50 copies.

STATEMENT of Officer Mack. Broadside.

STILES, HENRY R. The History of Ancient Windsor, Connecticut, including East Windsor, South Windsor and Ellington, prior to 1768, the date of their Separation from the Old Town; and Windsor, Bloomfield, and Windsor Locks to the present time; also the Genealogies and Genealogical Notes of those Families which settled within the limits of Ancient Windsor, Connecticut, prior to 1800. 8°, pp. xiv, 922.
700 copies.

TENTH Annual Report of the Albany County Penitentiary. 8°, pp. 64.
1,200 copies. These reports were all prepared by Samuel Pruyn until his death, and afterwards by Wm. A. Young and Gen. Amos Pilsbury.

TERMS and Circuits. 8°, pp. 20.
1,200 copies.

TRANCHEPAIN, ST. AUGUSTINE DE. Relation du Voyage des Premières Ursulines à la Nouvelle Orléans et de leur établissement en cette ville. Par la Rev. Mére St. Augustin de Tranchepain, Superieure. Avec les lettres circulaires quelques unes de ses Soeurs, et de la dite Mère. Small 8°, pp. 63.

TRANSACTIONS of the American Institute of Homœopathy, ior 1859; Sixteenth Annual Session, held in Boston, Mass. June 1, 1859. 8°, pp. 195.
500 copies.

TUTHILL, FRANKLIN. The Old Schools and the New; An Address delivered at the Closing Exercises of the Twenty-ninth Term of the New York State Normal School, Feb. 3, 1859. 8°, pp. 13.

TWENTY-THIRD Annual Report of the Albany City Tract and Missionary Society presented at the Annual Meeting, in the Second Presbyterian church, December 19, 1858. 8°, pp. 27.
1,200 copies.

VAN SCHAACK, ELIZA T. A Woman's Hand; or Plain Instructions for Embellishing a Cottage; with Easy and Practical Lessons in Pellis or Leather Work; Oriental; Grecian Oil, and Italian Landscape Paintings. 12°, pp. 58.
400 copies.

VAN SCHAACK, HENRY C. Henry Cruger, the Colleague of Edmund Burke, in the British Parliament, a paper read before the New York Historical Society, Jan. 4, 1859. 8°, pp. 67.
500 copies.

VOTES and Proceedings of the Assembly of the State of New York; at the first Meeting of the Fourth Session, begun and held at Poughkeepsie, in Dutchess County, on Thursday, September, 7th, 1780. Folio, pp. 59.
500 copies. Reprinted from the only copy known to exist of the journal of this Session. Although it was printed, no other copy could anywhere be found.

WILLARD, SYLVESTER D. Annual Address before the Medical Society of the County of Albany, Nov. 8, 1859. 8°, pp. 18.
300 copies.

WILLIAMS, WILLIAM H. Dealer in Housekeeping Articles, Wooden Ware Generally. Established in 1842, 75 State Street, one door from North Pearl Street, Albany, N. Y. 32°, pp. 32.

1860.

ADAMS, SAMPSON & Co. The Albany Directory for the year 1860; containing a General Directory of the Citizens, a Business Directory, and other Miscellaneous Matter. 8°, pp. 240.
1,400 copies.

ADAMS, SAMPSON & Co. Troy Directory. 12°, pp. 443.
900 copies.

ALBANY Methodist Sunday School Union, of the Methodist Episcopal Church, Organized June 19, 1854. 12°, pp. 28.
3,000 copies.

ANNUAL Catalogue of the Officers and Students of Hartwick Theological and Classical Seminary, for the Academic year ending Aug. 22, 1860. 8°, pp. 16.

ANNUAL Catalogue of the Officers and Students of the Sand Lake Collegiate Institute, Sand Lake, N. Y. 8°, pp. 16.

ARTICLES of Association and By-Laws of the Bethlehem Mutual Insurance Company. 16°, pp. 16.

ARTICLES of Association and By-Laws of the Watervliet Mutual Insurance Association. 12°, pp. 16.

BAYLEY, JAMES ROOSEVELT. Memoirs of the Right Reverend Simon Wm. Gabriel Bruté, D.D., first Bishop of Vincennes, with Sketches describing his Recollections of Scenes connected with the French Revolution, and Extracts from his Journal. Square 8°, pp. 223.
1,000 copies, 12mo ; 50 small 4to ; 6 large paper.

BEDORTHA, N. Practical Medication, or the Invalid's Guide ; with Directions for the Treatment of Disease. 12°, pp. 281.
1,000 copies.

BY-LAWS of Ark Lodge No. 48: adopted April, 5846 ; revised Feb., 5860. 16°, pp. 16.

BY-LAWS, Rules and Regulations of the Champion Base Ball Club of Albany ; organized March 19, 1859. 16°, pp. 8.

CAHILL, DR. The Holy Eucharist ; a Lecture delivered in the St. Joseph's Church, Albany, on Sunday Evening, March 4th, 1860. 8°, pp. 19.
500 copies.

CAMPBELL, SYLVIA. The Practical Cook Book: containing Recipes, Directions, &c., for Plain and Fancy Cooking, being the Result of twenty years Experience in that Art.
1,000 copies.

CASES in the Court of Appeals in the State of New York. 8°.
20 copies.

CASES in the Supreme Court of the State of New York. 8°.
12 copies.

CATALOGUE and Circular of the Albany Medical College. 8°, pp. 8.
5,000 copies.

CATALOGUE and Circular of the Young Ladies' Institute No. 4 High Street, nearly opposite the Capitol, Albany, N. Y. Founded 1842. 8°, pp. 15.
200 copies.

CATALOGUE of Mrs. Loveridge's School, and the Commencement Exercises on their Fifth (&c.) Anniversary. 8°, pp. 35.
450 copies.

CATALOGUE of the Hudson Female Academy. 8°, pp. 15.
700 copies.

CATALOGUE of the Law School of the University of Albany. Fall Term. 8°, pp. 7.
2,000 copies.

CATALOGUE of the Law School of the University of Albany. Spring Term. 8°, pp. 8.
3,500 copies.

CATALOGUE of the Library of the Second R. P. Dutch Church Sabbath School, Albany, N.Y. 16°, pp. 32.

CATALOGUE of the New York Alpha of the Phi Beta Kappa; Union College, Schenectady, July, 1860. 8°, pp. 48.
500 copies.

CATALOGUE of the Scholars' Library of the Sabbath School connected with the First Baptist Church of Albany; organized May 16, 1858. 18°, pp. 20.

CATHOLIC Hymns. 18°, pp. 71.
1,500 copies.

CHAMBERLAIN, DR. Electricity, the only reliable Therapeutic Agent. 8°, pp. 16.

CHRISTIAN Religion. 8°, pp. 30.
1,000 copies.

CIRCULAR and Catalogue of the Albany Female Academy. Founded A. D. 1814. Incorporated Feb. 16, 1821. 8°, pp. 23.
1,000 copies.

CONSTITUTION and By-Laws of Sandy Hill Division No. 252, of the Sons of Temperance of the State of New York; Instituted Feb. 14, 1859. 16°, pp. 16.

CONSTITUTION, By-Laws and Rules of Order of Firemans' Lodge, No. 19, I. O. of O. F. of Northern New York; organized March 10, 1837. 16°, pp. 30.

CONSTITUTION, By-Laws and Rules of Order of Silver-Lake Lodge, No. 106, I. O. of O. F. of Northern New York. 16°, pp. 30.

CONSTITUTION of St. George's Benevolent Society of Albany, N. Y. 16°, pp. 12.

CONSTITUTION of the Teachers' Association of the State of New York; organized July 30, 1845; incorporated 1859. 16°, pp. 8.

CONVERSATION between Dominie and Patrick, or the Bible vs. Papacy. 12°, pp. 120.
1,000 copies.

CORWIN, DAVID. Introductory Sermon, preached before the Rensselaerville Baptist Association, at Greenville, Sept. 19, 1860. 8°, pp. 8.

COUNCIL Journal of the Legislative Assembly of the Territory of Nebraska, sixth session, begun and held at Omaha City, Dec. 5, A. D. 1859. 8°, pp. 348.
500 copies.

[CRANDALL.] Family Register. 8°, pp. 8.
50 copies.

CROAKERS, by Joseph Rodman Drake and Fitz-Greene Halleck; first complete edition. 8°, viii, 191.
150 copies.

CRUIKSHANK, JAMES. The New York Teacher; a Monthly Periodical, devoted to the Cause of General Education, and to the Elevation of the Teachers' Profession. Vol. IX. 8°, pp. iv, 568.
2,800 copies.

DABLON, CLAUDE. Relation de ci qui s'est passé de plus remarquable aux Missions des Peres de la Compagnie de Jesus en la Nouvelle France les années 1673 à 1679. 8°, pp. xiv, 290.
160 copies; 5 on large paper.

DIARY of the Siege of Detroit in the War with Pontiac; also a Narrative of the Principal Events of the Siege, by Major Robert Rogers; a Plan for conducting Indian Affairs, by Col. Bradstreet; and other Authentick Documents, never before printed. Edited with notes by Franklin B. Hough. Cap 4°, pp. xvi, 304.
130 copies; 6 large paper.

ELEVENTH Annual Report of the Albany County Penitentiary. 8°, pp. 42.
1,200 copies.

FORTY-SEVENTH Annual Report of the Albany Female Academy. 8°, pp. 22.
1,000 copies.

FOURTH Annual Report of the Directors of the Mutual Insurance Association of Nassau, Schodack and Chatham. 12°, pp. 15.

GENDRON, SIEUR. Quelqves Particvlarities dv Pays des Hvrons eu la Novvelle France, remarquées par le Sieur Gendron, Docteur en Medecine, qui a demeure dans ce Pays-là fort long-temps. Redigées par Iean Baptiste de Rocoles, Conseiller, and Aumosnier du Roy, and Historiographe de sa Majesté. A. Troyes, & a Paris, M. DC. LX. 8°, pp. 26.

GOWANS. Catalogue of Ancient and Rare American Books, for Sale at the
affixed Prices, Stores 81, 83, and 84 Centre Street, New York. 8°,
pp. 20.
1,250 copies.

GOWANS. Catalogue of Books. 8°, pp. 40.
2,500 copies.

HAMOR, RALPH. A Trve Discovrse of the Present Estate of Virginia,
and the Success of the affaires there till the 18 of Iune, 1614. Together
with a relation of the severall English Townes and Fortes, the assured
hopes of that countrie and the peace concluded with the Indians, the
christning of Powhatan's Daughter and her Marriage with an Englishman; written by Raphe Hamor the yonger, late Secretarie in that
Colony. Alget, que non ardet. Printed at London by Iohn Beale
for William Welby dwelling at the signe of the Swanne in Pauls Church
yard, 1615. Folio, pp. viii, 70.
200 copies. Reprinted from original cap 4to copy in fac simile.

HOUSE Journal of the Legislative Assembly of the Territory of Nebraska,
sixth session; begun and held at Omaha City, Dec. 5, A. D. 1859. 8°,
pp. 406.
500 copies.

HOUGH, FRANKLIN B. A History of Lewis County, in the State of New
York, from the beginning of its settlement to the present time. 8°, pp.
iv, 319.
1,325 copies.

HUNTLEY, W. D. Instructions in Teaching Mental Arithmetic and Written Arithmetic. 12°, pp. 60.
300 copies.

LAKES of Central New York. Cayuga Lake, Cayuga Bridge, Taghkanic
Falls, on the Cayuga. The traveler will find the incidents of a day on
the Lakes worthy of his attention. 18°, pp. 8.
50 copies.

LAW Cases and Points in the Supreme Court of the State of New York.
8°.
12 copies.

LAW, WILLIAM. A Plain Account of the Nature and Ground of the
Christian Religion. 8°, pp. 30.

LAWS, Joint Resolutions and Memorials passed at the Sixth Session of the
Legislative Assembly of the Territory of Nebraska, begun and held at
Omaha City, N. T., Dec. 5, A. D. 1859; together with the Constitution
of the United States and the Organic Law. 8°, pp. 233.
2,500 copies.

LIST of Persons sent to the Penitentiary. 8°, pp. 12.
200 copies.

MANUAL of the Congregational Church in Union Village, Washington
County, N. Y. 12°, pp. 32.

MINUTES and Register of the Eighth Anniversary of the Saratoga Baptist Sabbath School Convention, held with the Glenville Baptist Church, Tuesday, Aug. 29, 1860. 16°, pp. 20.

MINUTES of the Evangelical Lutheran Ministerium of the State of New York. 8°, pp. 58.
750 copies.

MINUTES of the Particular Synod of Albany. 8°, pp. 34.
400 copies.

MINUTES of the Sixty-fourth Anniversary of the Rensselaerville Association, held in the Meeting House of the Baptist Church at Greenville, Greene County, N. Y., commencing Wednesday, Sept. 19, 1860. 8°, pp. 24.
800 copies.

MINUTES of the Twenty-first Annual Convention of the Hartwick Synod of the Evangelical Lutheran Church in the State of New York, held at Gallupville, Schoharie County, N. Y., September 13–18, 1861. 8°, pp. 45.
1,000 copies.

MORANGE, WILLIAM D. A Poem delivered at the Complimentary Concert of Geo. Wm. Warren, on the Occasion of the Opening of Tweddle Hall, June 28, 1860. 8°, pp. 15.

MUNSELL, JOEL. Catalogue of Books. 12°, pp. 36.
1,000 copies.

MUNSELL, JOEL. Catalogue of Books. 8°, pp. 12.
500 copies.

MUNSELL, JOEL. Webster's Calendar, or the Albany Almanac for the year of our Lord 1861. 12°, pp. 36.
35,000 copies.

NINTH Annual Catalogue of the Spencertown Academy, Spencertown, N. Y. 8°, pp. 12.

OBITUARY on the Death of Ann Coleman, a Member of the Arbor Hill M. E. Sabbath School, Albany, who died Sept. 15, 1859, aged 13 years. 16°, pp. 13.

ONE Hundred and Seventh Annual Catalogue of the Officers and Students of Columbia College, including the Law and Medical Departments, and the Grammar School for 1860–61. 8°, pp. 111.

ORDERLY Book of Lieut. Gen. John Burgoyne, from his Entry into the State of New York until his Surrender at Saratoga, 16th Oct., 1777, from the Original Manuscript deposited at Washington's Head Quarters, Newburgh, N. Y.; Edited by E. B. O'Callaghan. 4°, pp. xxxiv, 221.
200 copies; 10 large paper. Map, 4 portraits and plate.

ORDERLY Book of that Portion of the American Army stationed at or near Williamsburg, Va., under the command of Gen. Andrew Lewis, from March 18th, 1776 to August 28th, 1776; printed from the Original Manuscript, with Notes and Introduction by Charles Campbell. Cap 4°, pp. xii, 100.
200 copies; 10 large paper.

PHELPS, RICHARD H. A History of Newgate of Connecticut, at Simsbury, now East Granby; its Insurrections and Massacres, the Imprisonment of the Tories in the Revolution, and the working of its Mines; also, some account of the State Prison at Wethersfield. Cap. 4°, pp. 151.
300 copies. Portrait of Amos Pilsbury and engravings.

POINTS in the Court of Appeals of the State of New York. 8°.
20 copies.

POINTS in the Supreme Court of the State of New York. 8°.
12 copies.

[PRUYN, SAMUEL.] Life of Amos Pilsbury. 8°, pp. 44.
500 copies.

REDFIELD, JOHN HOWARD. Genealogical History of the Redfield Family in the United States; being a revision and extension of the Genealogical Tables compiled in 1839 by William C. Redfield. 8°, pp. viii, 337.
350 copies.

REMINISCENCES of Troy, from its Settlement in 1790 to 1807, with Remarks on its Commerce, Enterprise and Improvement, State of Political Parties, and Sketches of Individual Character; written at the request of several gentlemen of Troy, by John Woodworth: second Edition, with Notes, Explanatory, Biographical, Historical and Antiquarian. Cap 4°, pp. iv, 112.
250 copies.

REPORT of Pittsburgh Board of Trade. 8°, pp. 36.
500 copies.

REPORT of the Forty-seventh Annual Examination of the Albany Female Academy; and of the Exercises of the Alumnæ of the Institution, on their Nineteenth Anniversary, June 19, 1860. 8°, pp. 22.

REPORT of the Free Bethel, formerly the Floating Bethel, for 1859 and 1860, located at the Little Basin. 8°, pp. 4.

REPORTS of Grand Officers. 8°, pp. 22.

ROESSLE, THEOPHILUS. Roessle's Gardener's Hand Books, No. 1. How to cultivate and preserve Celery. Edited with a preface by Henry S. Olcott. 12°, pp. 100.
1,000 copies. 4 Plates.

RUTTENBER, E. M. Obstructions to the Navigation of Hudson's River; embracing the Minutes of the Secret Committee appointed by the Provincial Convention of New York, July 16, 1776, and other Original Documents relating to the Subject; together with Papers relating to the Beacons. Cap 4°, pp. viii, 210.
125 copies; 6 on large paper. Map.

SALES, ABRAM. Original and Interesting Book on the Horse, showing the Characteristics of this Noble Animal, interspersed with Anecdotes, etc., together with a large number of Valuable and original Recipes, collected during a career of thirty years, among the Indians, and from Practical Experience, and now offered to the Public for the first time. 12°, pp. 104.

1,000 copies.

SARGENT, WINTHROP. The Loyal Verses of Joseph Stansbury and Doctor Jonathan Odell; relating to the American Revolution. Cap 4°, pp. xxiv, 199.

150 copies; 10 large paper.

SEVENTEENTH Annual Report of the Albany City Missionary Society, presented May 29th, 1860. 12°, pp. 24.

1,000 copies.

SHEA, JOHN GILMARY. A French Onondaga Dictionary, from a Manuscript of the Seventeenth Century. 8°, pp. 103.

150 copies; 10 large paper.

SIMMS, JEPTHA R. Trappers of New York, or a Biography of Nicholas Stoner and Nathaniel Foster; together with Anecdotes of other celebrated Hunters, and some Account of Sir William Johnson, and his Style of Living. 12°, pp. 287.

Plates.

SMITH, WM. R. The Jurisdiction of Justices of the Peace in Civil and Criminal Cases, with Forms for the Use of Executors, Guardians, Administrators, and Civil Officers. All Arranged under the Laws of the State of Alabama, as now in force. Third Edition with numerous Forms for Conveyances. 8°, pp. 260.

2,000 copies.

SMITH, WM. R. The Uses of Solitude. 8°, pp. 64.

500 copies.

TERMS and Circuits of the Supreme Court, Circuit Courts, and Courts of Oyer and Terminer, of the State of New York, from the 1st of Jan., 1860 to 1st of Jan., 1862. 8°, pp. 20.

THIRD Annual Catalogue of the Officers and Students of the Law School of Columbia College, for 1860–61. 8°, pp. 32.

TWENTY-FIFTH Annual Announcement of the Troy Conference Academy, Poultney, Vt., for the Academic year commencing Aug. 16, 1860. 32°, pp. 8.

5,500 copies.

TWENTY-FOURTH Annual Report of the Albany City Tract and Missionary Society, presented at the Annual Meeting in the North Pearl Street Baptist Church, December 18, 1859. 8°, pp. 28.

1,200 copies.

WHITE, PFISTER & Co.   Catalogue of Books.   8°, pp. 8.
500 copies.

WHITE, PFISTER & Co.   Catalogue of Law Books.   8°, pp. 47.
1,000 copies.

WHITTLESEY, ELISHA.   Christian Resignation; a Sermon on the Death
of Henry Colton Skinner, preacher in the Presbyterian Church, Le
Roy, N. Y., Dec. 6, 1859.   8°, pp. 30.
75 copies.

WILLARD, SAMUEL G.   Annual Report of the Windham Association and
Consociation for 1859.   8°, pp. 8.
1,500 copies.

WOOLEY, CHARLES.   A Two Years Journal in New York; and part of
its Territories in America; a new edition with an Introduction and
copious Historical Notes, by E. B. O'Callaghan, M.D.   8°, pp. 97.
500 copies; 50 on large paper.

1861.

ALBANY Directory for the year 1861; containing a General Directory of
the Citizens, a Business Directory, a Record of the city Government,
its Institutions, &c.   8°, pp. 204, 38.
1,400 copies.

ANNUAL Catalogue of the Officers and Students of Hartwick Theological
and Classical Seminary, for the Academic year ending Aug. 28, 1861.
8°, pp. 12.

BOARD of Trade.   Constitution and By-Laws of the City of Albany.   8°,
pp. 12.

BOARD of Trade.   Review of the Trade and Commerce of the City of
Albany, for the year 1861.   8°, pp. 71.

BURY, RICHARD DE.   Philobiblon, a Treatise on the Love of Books, by
Richard de Bury, Bishop of Durham and Lord Chancellor of England;
First American Edition, with the Literal English Translation of John
B. Inglis, collated and corrected, with Notes by Samuel Hand.   Small
8°, pp. x, 252.
200 copies small; 30 large.

CIRCULAR and Catalogue of the Albany Female Academy,   Founded
A. D. 1814.   Incorporated Feb. 16, 1821.   8°, pp. 23.
1,000 copies.

CONSTITUTION and By-Laws of Grand Encampment, I. O. of O. F.   8°,
pp. 56.
250 copies.

COUNCIL Journal of the Legislative Assembly of the Territory of Nebraska, seventh Session; begun and held at Omaha City, Dec. 3, A. D. 1860. 8°, pp. 268.

CRUIKSHANK, JAMES. The New York Teacher; a Monthly Periodical, devoted to the Cause of General Education, and to the Elevation of the Teachers' Profession. Vol. X. 8°, pp. 568.
2,000 copies.

CUESTA, FELIPE ARROGO DE LA. Grammar of the Mutsun Language spoken at the Mission of San Juan Bautista, Alta California. 8°, pp. 48.
160 copies.

DABLON, CLAUDE. Relation de ce qui s'est passé de plus Remarquable aux Missions des Peres de la Compagnie de Jesus en la Nouvelle France les années 1672 et 1673. 8°, pp. v, 220.
160 copies.

[DYER, DAVID.] Fiftieth Annual Report of the Albany County Bible Society, and the Semi-Centennial Sermon. 8°, pp. 35.
1,000 copies.

EXERCISES of the Alumnæ of the Albany Female Academy, on their Twentieth Anniversary, on Monday, June 17, 1861. 8°, pp. 56.

F.A.T.A.L. Book of Instructions. 8°, pp. 39.
250 copies.

FIFTH Annual Report of the Directors of the Mutual Insurance Association of Nassau, Schodack and Chatham. 12°, pp. 15.

FORTY-NINTH Annual Report of the Albany County Bible Society. 12°, pp. 14.
1,000 copies.

FOURTH Annual Catalogue of the Officers and Students of the Law School of Columbia College for 1861–1862. 8°, pp. 32.
500 copies.

GENERAL Orders, Camp Morgan, June, 1851. 8°, pp. 7.

GOULD, JAMES. A Treatise on the Principles of Pleading, in Civil Actions, by James Gould. Fourth Edition, with Notes, adapted to the New York Code of Procedure, by George Gould, one of the Justices of the Supreme Court of the State of New York. 8°, pp. xiv, 502.

GOWANS. Catalogue of Old English Books, for sale at the affixed Prices. Store 81, 83 and 85 Centre Street, New York. 8°, pp. 40.

HOUSE Journal of the Legislative Assembly of the Territory of Nebraska, fifth Session, begun and held at Omaha City, Sept. 21, A. D. 1858. 8°, pp. 345.
500 copies.

HYMNS for Sunday Schools. 12°, pp. 72.
1,500 copies.

JONES, DANIEL T. Annual Address before the Medical Society of the State of New York and Members of the Legislature, in the Capitol, Feb. 5, 1861. 8°, pp. 15.

JOURNAL of the Twenty-fourth Annual Session of the Frankean Evangelical Lutheran Synod, convened at Argusville, Schoharie county, N. Y. Thursday, June 6, 1861. 8°, pp. 32.
700 copies.

LAW Cases and Points in the Supreme Court of the State of New York. 8°.
12 copies.

LAW Cases in the Court of Appeals of the State of New York. 8°.
20 copies.

LAW Points in the Court of Appeals of the State New York. 2 vols. 8°,
20 copies.

LAW Points in the Supreme Court of the State of New York. 2 vols. 8°.
12 copies.

LAWS and Joint Resolutions and Memorials passed at the Seventh Session of the Legislative Assembly of the Territory of Nebraska, begun and held at Omaha City, N. T., December 5, A. D. 1860: together with the Constitution of the United States and the Organic Law. Published by Authority. 8°, pp. 270.
2,500 copies.

LAWS of the State of New York passed at the Eighty-fourth Session of the Legislature, begun January first and ended April sixteenth, 1861, in the city of Albany. 8°, pp. 913.
5,000 copies.

LUCKENBACH, W. H. On Magnifying God's Work: a Thanksgiving Discourse preached in the Dutch Reformed Church at Rhinebeck, on Thursday, Nov. 28, 1861. 8°, pp. 24.

MINUTES of the Particular Synod of Albany. 8°, pp. 34.
400 copies.

MINUTES of the Sixty-fifth Anniversary of the Rensselaerville Association, held in the Meeting House of the Baptist Church at Preston Hollow, Greene county, N. Y., commencing Wednesday, Sept. 4, 1861. 8°, pp. 12.
800 copies.

MINUTES of the Sixty-sixth Synod of the Evangelical Lutheran Ministerium of the State of New York, and Adjacent States and Countries, held in the German Evangelical Lutheran Church of Zion, at Rochester, New York, commencing on Friday, Aug. 30, 1861, and ending on Wednesday, Sept. 4, 1861. 8°, pp. 79.
750 copies.

MINUTES of the Thirty-first Annual Convention of the Hartwick Synod of the Evangelical Lutheran Church in the State of New York, held at Gallupville, Schoharie county, N. Y., Sept. 13–18, 1861. 8°, pp. 45.
1,500 copies.

MNEMONICS. A New and Ingenious System of Written Mnemonics; illustrated by copious examples from Moral Philosophy, Science and Religion, and followed by the Explanation (Part II), containing all the Information necessary to make Part I, plain and intelligible. 18°, pp. 135.
    1,000 copies.

MUNSELL, JOEL. Webster's Calendar, or the Albany Almanac for the year of our Lord 1862. 12°, pp. 36.

O'CALLAGHAN, E. B. A List of Editions of the Holy Scriptures and Parts thereof, printed in America previous to 1860; with Introduction and Bibliographical Notes. Royal 8°, pp. lxii, 415.
    250 copies.

ONE Hundred and Eighth Annual Catalogue of the Officers and Students of Columbia College, including the Law and Medical Departments, and the Grammar School for 1861–62. 8°, pp. 91.
    3,000 copies.

PRATT, GEORGE W. An Account of the British Expedition above the Highlands of the Hudson River, and of the Events connected with the burning of Kingston in 1777, read before the Ulster Historical Society. 4°, pp. 73.
    50 copies.

PROCEEDINGS of the Commissioners of Indian Affairs, appointed by Law for the Extinguishment of Indian Titles in the State of New York; published from the original Manuscript in the Library of the Albany Institute; with an Introduction and Notes, by Franklin B. Hough. 2 vols., 4°, pp. 501.
    200 copies small; 10 large. 3 maps.

[RAWSON, T. R.] Eighteenth Annual Report of the Albany City Missionary Society, presented May 26th, 1861. 12°, pp. 12.
    150 copies.

REED, SYLVANUS. The Duty of the Citizen in these Times: a Sermon preached in the Church of the Holy Innocents, Albany, Sunday morning, April 21, 1861. 8°, pp. 15.

REPORT of the Forty-Eighth Annual Examination of the Albany Female Academy, presented at their Anniversary, Tuesday, June 18, 1861. 8°, pp. 23.
    1,000 copies.

REPORT of the Third Annual Examination of Mrs. Loveridge's School. and the commencement Exercises on their Sixth (&c.) Anniversary. 8°, pp. 36.
    450 copies.

RUDDER, WILLIAM. The Complete Physician; an Address pronounced before the Graduates of the Albany Medical College, in the Assembly Chamber, Dec. 24, 1860. 8°, pp. 30.
    500 copies.

RUDDER, WILLIAM. The Educational Powers of our present National Troubles; a Sermon preached in St. Paul's Church, Albany, on Sunday Evening, Jan. 13, 1861. 8°, pp. 35.

SHEA, JOHN GILMARY. Early Voyages up and down the Mississippi, by Cavelier, St. Cosme, Le Seur, Gravier, and Guignas. With Introduction, Notes, and an Index. Cap 4°, pp. 191.

SITJAR, BONAVENTURE. Vocabulary of the Language of San Antonio Mission, California. 8°, pp. xix, 53.
  160 copies.

SQUIER, E. G. Monograph of Authors who have written on the Languages of Central America, and collected Vocabularies or composed Works in the Native Dialects of that Country. Square 8°, pp. 70.
  100 copies; 10 large paper.

THIRD Annual Report of the Windham County Association. 8°, pp. 8.
  1,500 copies.

TROY Directory for the year 1861; with a Business Directory, and other Miscellaneous Matter, also Directories of West Troy, Green Island and Lansingburgh. 12°, pp. 436, 20.
  1,000 copies.

TWENTY-FIFTH Annual Report of the Albany City Tract and Missionary Society, presented at the Annual Meeting in the First Presbyterian Church, December 23, 1860. 8°, pp. 27.
  1,200 copies.

WETMORE, JAMES CARNAHAN. The Wetmore Family in America, and its Collateral Branches; with Genealogical, Biographical and Historical Notices; Royal 8°, pp. xii, 670.
  500 copies.

WHITE, PFISTER & Co.'s Catalogue of English and American Books; a choice and carefully selected assortment of the Best Works in every Department of Literature. 8°, pp. 46.

WHITE, PFISTER & Company, Exchange Corner, Montgomery, Alabama. General Catalogue of Law Books. 8°, pp. 8.

WOODWORTH's Planing Machines, built by Daniel Doncaster, 198 and 200 Water Street, Albany, N. Y. 12°, pp. 16.

1862.

ALBANY Directory for the year 1862, containing a General Directory of the Citizens, a Business Directory, a Record of the City Government, its Institutions, &c., &c. 8°, pp. 252.
  1,400 copies.

AN DIE Deutschen Wähler der Stadt Albany. 8°, pp. 8.

ANNUAL Catalogue of the Officers and Students of Hartwick Theological and Classical Seminary, for the Academical year ending Aug. 27. 1862. 8°, pp. 12.
  300 copies.

ANTHEMS. Mary Warren Free Institute. 12°, pp. 57.
  500 copies.

ARGUMENT of John K. Porter in the Parish Will Case. 8°, pp. 72.
600 copies.

BIBLIOTHECA Curiosa; Catalogue [No. 4.] of Superior New and Second
Hand Ancient and Modern English Books, in all Departments of Literature, lately received and for Sale by J. W. Bouton & Co., 87 Walker St.,
a few doors east of Broadway, New York. 8°, pp. 20.
2,000 copies.

BOARD of Trade. Second Annual Report of the City of Albany, for the
year 1862. pp. 56.

BOYD, ANDREW. Boyd's Rome Directory and Oneida County Business
Directory (classified according to Trade), a Record of the Rebellion of
1861, with Sketches of American and other Wars; and an Appendix
of much General Information. 12°, pp. 211.
250 copies.

BOYD, ANDREW. Directory of Poughkeepsie. 12°, pp. 198.

BRADT, HENRY Y. Schenectady City and County Directory for 1862–3,
containing the names of Residents and a List of City and County
Officers, together with Valuable Miscellaneous Matter. 12°, pp. 141.
180 copies.

BROTHERHEAD, W. General Fremont and the Injustice done him by
Politicians and envious Military Men. 8°, pp. 10.
500 copies.

BY-LAWS and Catalogue of Books, in the Franklin Library Association.
Hudson, N. Y. 12°, pp. 48.
600 copies.

CATALOGUE and Circular of the Albany Medical College. 8°, pp. 12.
10,000 copies.

CATALOGUE [No. 5] of a Large Collection of Superior New and Second
Hand Ancient and Modern English Books, just received from London
per ship Yorktown [etc.] for Sale by J. W. Bouton & Co., 87 Walker
Street, a few doors East of Broadway, New York. 8°, pp. 24.

CATALOGUE of Columbia College Law School. 8°.
1,000 copies.

CATALOGUE of the Albany Female Academy. Founded A. D. 1814.

CATALOGUE of the North Dutch Church Sabbath School Library. 16°,
pp. 32.

CATALOGUE of the Officers and Members of the Warren County Teachers'
Association for A. D. 1861–2; also, of the Teachers and Students of
the Warren County Teachers' Institute held at Warrensburgh, for 1861.
12°, pp. 12.

CATALOGUE of the Officers and Students of the Sand Lake Collegiate
Institute, Sand Lake, N. Y. 8°.
1,000 copies.

CATALOGUE of the Schoharie County Teachers' Institute, held at Sharon Springs, commencing Oct. 26, and closing Nov. 1, 1861. 8°, pp. 16.
200 copies.

CATALOGUE of W. Brotherhead's Circulating Library, No. 218 South Eighth Street, Philadelphia. 8°, pp. 40.
5,000 copies.

CHRISTMAS Stories. 16°, pp. 20.

CONSTITUTION, Rules and Orders of the Associated Congress of the Law Department of the University of Albany. 16°, pp. 14.
4,500 copies.

CRUIKSHANK, JAMES. The New York Teacher, a Monthly Journal of School and Home Education. Vol. XI. 8°, pp. iv, 508.
1,700 copies.

CUESTA, FELIPE ORROGO DE LA. A Vocabulary or Phrase Book of the Mutsun Language of Alta California. 8°, pp. 96.
160 copies.

DRAKE, SAMUEL G. A Brief Memoir of Sir Walter Raleigh; prepared for and published in the New England Historical and Genealogical Register for April, 1862, and now reprinted with Additions. 4to, pp. 35.
120 copies large paper.

DRAKE, SAMUEL G. The History of King Philip's War, by the Rev. Increase Mather, D.D. Also, a History of the same War, by the Rev. Cotton Mather, D.D. To which are added an Introduction and Notes, by Samuel G. Drake. 4°, pp. 282.
250 copies; 13 large paper. Portraits of Increase and Cotton Mather.

DUNNEL, HENRY GALE. The True Genealogy of the Dunnel and Dwinell Family of New England. 8°, pp. 84.
300 copies.

DURRIE, DANIEL STEELE. Steele Family. A Genealogical History of John and George Steele (settlers of Hartford, Conn.), 1635–6, and their Descendants. With an Appendix, containing Genealogical information respecting other families of the name who settled in different parts of the United States. Enlarged edition. Royal 8°, pp. x, 161.
150 copies. Merely Appendix and new title.

DYER, DAVID. A Sermon. 8°, pp. 20.
200 copies.

FIFTY-FIRST Annual Report of the Albany County Bible Society, with the Annual Sermon, by Rev. E. Halley, D.D. 8°, pp. 26.
500 copies.

FOURTEENTH Annual Report of the Albany County Penitentiary. 8°, pp. 40.
1,200 copies.

FOURTH Annual Report of the Bible Society of Fulton and Hamilton Counties, presented at Broadalbin, Sept. 2, 1861, with Statistics. 8°, pp. 21.
500 copies.

FOURTH Annual Report of Windham Association, Consociation and Benevolent Association, with Statistics of 1862, for the Churches. 8°, pp. 4.
1,000 copies.

FROST, SARAH E. A[NDREWS]. A Coat of Many Colors. 12°, pp. 300.
500 copies.

GENEALOGIES, &c. 8°.

Memoir of Hon. Nahum Mitchell. pp. 4.	Lombard Family. pp. 2.
Vickers or Vickery Family. pp. 3.	Gale Family. pp. 9,
Epitaph Rev. John Ward. pp. 2.	Forth Family. pp. 1.
Tercentenary of Birth Shakespeare. 4.	Clopton Family. pp. 1.
One Branch of Adams Family. pp. 1.	Tyndale Family. pp. 1,
Will of Herbert Pelham. pp. 3.	Townes Family. pp. 1.
Windsor Family Munsell. pp. 8.	Barnaby Family. pp. 3.
	Babcock Family. pp. 4.

These were printed during the years 1862, 1863 and 1864, from the New England
Historical and Genealogical Register, and are without date, mostly, and have been
bound in one volume.

GOWANS, WM. Catalogue of Books. 8°, pp. 40.
2,500 copies.

HACKETT, W. V. The Hudson City and Columbia County Directory, for
the year 1862-3, with an Appendix containing a Record of the Soldiers
of the City and County, and a Variety of Useful Information. 12°,
pp. 208.
400 copies.

HARRIS, EDWARD DOUBLEDAY. The Vassals of New England and their
immediate Descendants, a Genealogical and Biographical Sketch, compiled from Church and Town Records. 8°, pp. 26.

HAYNES. Troy Almanac for 1862. 12°, pp. 36.

HEMENWAY, ABBY MARIA. The Vermont Gazetteer. 8°, pp. 96.
6,000 copies.

HITCHCOCK, O. B. Elegiac and Letter on Col. William A. Jackson. 12°,
pp. 4.

JOGUES, ISAAC. Novum Belgium: an Account of New Netherland in
1643-4. By Rev. Father Isaac Jogues, of the Society of Jesus. With
a fac simile of his original Manuscript, his Portrait, a Map, and Notes
by John Gilmary Shea. 4to, pp. 53.
150 copies, large paper. Lacks portrait and fac simile manuscript.

JOGUES, ISAAC. Novum Belgium, description de New Netherland et
Notices sur René Goupil. Par le R. P. Isaac Jogues, de la Compagnie
de Jesus. Small 8°, pp. 44.
100 copies.

LAW Cases and Points in the Court of Appeals of the State of New York.
8°.
20 copies.

LAW Points in the Supreme Court of the State of New York. 8°.
  12 copies.

LAWYER, JOHN D. ΑΠΟΚΑΛΥΨΙΣ. A Revelation from Jesus the
  Christ communicated to John the Evangelist. Being a correct transla-
  lation and Exposition for a true understanding of the same. 12°, pp. 60.
  500 copies.

LEWIS, WINSLOW. Annual Address of the President of the New England
  Historic-Genealogical Society, delivered Jan. 6, 1862. 8°, pp. 9.

LITTLE Office of the Immaculate Conception. 16°, pp. 15.

LIVERMORE, S. T. A Condensed History of Cooperstown, with a Biographical Sketch of J. Fennimore Cooper. 12°, pp. 276.
  600 copies.

McCLELLAN, ROBERT H. The Executor's Guide; a complete Manual for
  Executors, Administrators and Guardians, with a full Exposition of
  their Rights, Privileges, Duties and Liabilities, and of the Rights of
  Widows in the Personal Estate, and to Dower, with Forms. 12°,
  pp. 205.
  1,500 copies.

MEMOIR of William A. Jackson, a Member of the Albany Bar, and Colonel
  of the 18th Regiment N. Y. Volunteers, who died at the City of
  Washington, Nov. 11, 1861. 8°, pp. 40.

MILLER, JOHN. A Description of the Province and City of New York,
  with Plans of the City and several Forts as they existed in the year
  1695. A New Edition with an Introduction and Copious Historical
  Notes, by John Gilmary Shea. 8°, pp. 127.
  500 copies; 50 large paper.

MINUTES of Particular Synod of Albany. 8°, pp. 36.
  400 copies.

MINUTES of the Sixty-seventh Synod of the Evangelical Lutheran Ministerium of the State of New York, and adjacent States and Countries,
  held in the German Evangelical Lutheran Church of St. John, at New-
  ark, N. J., commencing Saturday, Sept. 6, and ending Wednesday,
  Sept. 10, 1862. 8°, pp. 70.
  750 copies.

MUNSELL, JOEL. Webster's Calendar, or the Albany Almanac for the
  year of our Lord 1863. 12°, pp. 36.

NEW England Historical and Genealogical Register, published Quarterly
  under the Patronage of the New England Historic-Genealogical Society, for the year 1862. 8°, vol. XVI, pp. iv, 397.
  600 copies. 4 plates.

NEW Law Books published by William Gould (of the late firm of Gould,
  Banks & Co.), Law Bookseller and Publisher, No. 60 State Street,
  Albany, N. Y. 8°, pp. 8.

OBITUARIES of Deceased Members of the New England Historic-Genealogical Society. 8°, pp. 40.

PROCEEDINGS [of the Board of Supervisors of the County of Washington]. 8°, pp. 34.

[RAWSON, T. R.] Nineteenth Annual Report of the Albany City Missionary Society, presented June 19, 1862. 12°, pp. 12.

REPORT of the Eighth Annual Examination of Mrs. Loveridge's School, and the Commencement Exercises on their Eighth (&c.) Anniversary. 8°.

REVIEW of the Trade and Commerce of the City of Albany, for the year 1861. 8°, pp. 71.
2,000 copies. Prepared by Wm. Lacy.

SERMON, delivered at the Funeral of Mr. Nathan Ball, who departed this Life December 29th, 1797, in the 62d year of his Age. Printed at Lee, Jan. 13, 1800, by Cyrus Yale. 8°, pp. 22.
100 copies.

SHEPPARD, JOHN H. A Brief History of the New England Historic-Genealogical Society, read before the Monthly Meeting, May 7, 1862. 8°, pp. 17.

SHEPPARD, JOHN H. Sketch of Hon. Nathan Appleton, LL.D. 8°, pp. 12.

SIMS, STANLEY CLIFFORD. The Origin and Signification of Scottish Surnames, with a Vocabulary of Christian Names. 8°, pp. 125.
250 copies.

SMITH, BUCKINGHAM. Doctrina Christiana y Confessionario en Lengua Nevome, ō sea la Pima, propia de Sonora. 8°, pp. 32.
160 copies; 80 large paper.

SMITH, BUCKINGHAM. Grammar of the Pima or Névome, a Language of Sonora, from a Manuscript of the XVII Century. 8°, pp. 97.
160 copies; 80 large paper.

THE Quarter Century Anniversary Celebration of the Ministry of the Rev. Dr. Wyckoff, in the Second Reformed Dutch Church, Albany, Nov. 3, 1861. 8°, pp. 32.
400 copies.

THOMPSON's Calendar or the Chenango Almanac for the year of our Lord 1862. 12°, pp. 36.
5,000 copies.

TREASURER's Report. Annual Report of the Treasurers of Union College. Made June 30, 1862. Printed for the Trustees and Visitors. [Not published.] 8°, pp. 22.
75 copies.

TROY Almanac and Franklin Calendar for the year of our Lord, 1862. 12°, pp. 36.

TWENTY-SIXTH Annual Report of the City Tract and Missionary Society, presented at the Annual Meeting, in the Second Presbyterian Church, December 22, 1861. 8°, pp. 23.
1,200 copies.

ULSTER and Delaware County Farmers Almanac for the year of our Lord 1862. 12°, pp. 36.

UNION COLLEGE.   Catalogue.   8°, pp. 48.
1,000 copies.

UNION COLLEGE.   Catalogue of Union College, First Term.   8°, pp. 44.
500 copies.

UNION COLLEGE Magazine.   8°, pp. 68.
200 copies.

UNION COLLEGE.   Union Resumé.   Folio.
700 copies.

UNIVERSITY of the State of New York: Colleges and Academies subject to the Visitation of the Regents of the University. 8°, pp. 13.

VAN LOAN's Farmers' Almanac, for the year of our Lord 1862. 12°, pp. 36.

WHITMORE, WILLIAM H.   A Handbook of American Genealogy; being a Catalogue of Family Histories and Publications containing Genealogical Information, chronologically arranged. 4°, pp. xxxii, 272.
200 copies small; 10 large paper.

WILLARD's Troy Almanac, for the year of our Lord 1862. 12°, pp. 36.

WILBUR, H. B.   Some Suggestions on the Principles and Methods of Elementary Instruction. 8°, pp. 31.

1863.

ALBANY Directory for the year 1863, containing a General Directory of the Citizens, a Business Directory, a Record of the City Government, its Institutions, &c., &c. 8°, pp. 264.
1,300 copies.

ANNUAL Catalogue of the Officers and Students of Hartwick Theological and Classical Seminary, for the Academic year ending Aug. 26, 1863. 8°, pp. 12.
300 copies.

BACKUS, J. T.   Address at Union College. 8°, pp. 45.
500 copies. Not on file.

BARKER, GEORGE F.   The Forces of Nature; an Address delivered before the Chemical Society of Union College, July 22, 1863. 8°, pp. 46.
200 copies.

BIDWELL, IRA G.   Faith in the Unseen, Man's only Satisfaction and Dignity; a Sermon preached in the Chapel of Union College, on the Annual Fast Day for Colleges, Feb. 26, 1863. 8°, pp. 16.

BOARD of Trade. Third Annual Report of the Trade and Commerce of the City of Albany, for the year 1863. 8°, pp. 50.

BOUTON's Catalogue of Books. Square 8°.
1,500 copies.

BOYD, A. Cleveland Directory. 8°, pp. 164.
550 copies.

BOYD, A. Newport Directory. ·12°, pp. 128.
375 copies.

BUNKER Hill Battle, by Col. S. Swett. 8°, pp. 12.
300 copies.

CATALOGUE and Circular of Albany Medical College. 8°, pp. 8.
5,000 copies.

CATALOGUE of Baptist Sabbath School Library. 16°.
500 copies.

CATALOGUE of Cottage Hill Seminary for Young Ladies, Poughkeepsie, Dutchess County, N. Y., Rev. George T. Rider, M. A. Rector. 8°, pp. 15.

CATALOGUE of the Cohoes District School Library June 1, 1864. 8°, pp. 41.
175 copies.

CATALOGUE of the Law School. 8°.
6,500 copies.

CATALOGUE of the Library of the Philomathean Society, in Union College. 1863. Founded Oct. 17, 1793. 12°, pp. 110.
300 copies.

CATALOGUE of Union College Senior Class. 8°, pp. 34.
700 copies. Not on file.

CELEBRATION of the Semi-Centennial Anniversary of the Albany Academy. Albany, June 23, 1863. 8°, pp. 188.
500 copies. Plate.

CIRCULAR and Catalogue of the Albany Female Academy. Founded A. D. 1814. Incorporated Feb. 16, 1821. 8°, pp. 24.
1,000 copies.

COCHRANE, C. B. Centennial Address at New Boston, N. H. 8°, pp. 44.
50 copies.

COLUMBIA COLLEGE. One Hundred and Ninth Annual Catalogue of the Officers and Students of Columbia College, including the Law and Medical Departments, and the Grammar School for 1862-1863. 8°, pp. 119, 56.
700 copies.

COLUMBIA COLLEGE. Fifth Annual Catalogue of the Officers and Students of the Law School of Columbia College, for 1862-63, with the Triennial Catalogue of the Alumni. pp. 48.
750 copies.

COLUMBIA COLLEGE. School of Chemistry, Columbia College, East Forty-Ninth Street, New York. pp. 8.
200 copies.

CONSTITUTION and By-Laws of St. Patrick's Library Society, organized Nov. 19, 1862. 16°, pp. 16.

CONSTITUTION and By-Laws of the Chemical Society of Union College. 12°, pp. 8.
500 copies.

CONSTITUTION of Engine Company No. 13. 16°, pp. 27.
500 copies.

CONSTITUTION of the Third Reformed Protestant Dutch Church Sabbath School, Albany, N. Y. 16°.
100 copies.

CRUIKSHANK, JAMES. The New York Teacher, a Monthly Journal of School and Home Education. Vol. XII, 8°, pp. 434.
1,500 copies.

DAVIS, W. P. Sermon. 8°, pp. 22.
300 copies.

DEAN, JOHN WARD. A Brief History of the New England Historical and Genealogical Register, being the Preface to the seventeenth Volume of that Work. 8°, pp. 8.

DEAN, JOHN WARD. Memoir of Rev. Michael Wigglesworth. 8°.
100 copies.

DEDERICK, F. C. Sermon. 12°.
500 copies.

DIGEST of Rules of Windham County Association, Revision of 1862. 16°, pp. 16.

D.K.E. Songs. (Union College.) 12°, pp. 54.
400 copies.

EDWARDS. In Memory of Carlton Edwards. 12°, pp. 272.
200 copies. Portrait. Introduction by Isaac Edwards, and selection by him.

EGGLESTON, C. M. A Funeral Discourse in Memory of Capt. Ayers G. Barker, 120th Reg. N. Y. S. V., late of Greenville, N. Y., killed at the Battle of Gettysburgh, July 26, 1863. 12°, pp. 19.

EXERCISES performed at the Burial of Mechanics, by the Junior Class of Union College, July 13, 1863. 8°, pp. 30.
500 copies.

FAIRBAIRN, R. B. Sermon. 8°, pp. 20.
500 copies.

FIELD, OSGOOD. A Genealogical Sketch of the Family of Field, of the West Riding of Yorkshire, England, and of Flushing and Newtown, in Long Island, N. Y., with a Tabular Pedigree. 8°, pp. 12 and folding pedigree.

FIFTH Annual Report of the Association, Consociation and Benevolent Association, with the Doings of the Conference and Ecclesiastical Statistics for A. D. 1863, Windham County, Conn. 8°, pp. 8.
1,400 copies.

FIFTY-SECOND Annual Report of the Albany County Bible Society, organized A. D. 1810.　8°, pp. 14.
　500 copies.

FISHER, SAMUEL W.　The Mission of the Teacher; an Address before the Graduating Class of the State Normal School, Jan. 29, 1863.　8°.
　800 copies.

GILMAN, ARTHUR.　A Genealogical and Biographical Record of that Branch of the Family of Gilman, descended from the Honorable Counsellor John Gilman, of Exeter, N. H., with which is incorporated some Account of his Ancestors and the English Branch of the Gilman Family. 8°, pp. 51.
　100 copies.

GOWANS.　Clearing out Sale of Surplus Books before bidding Farewell to Egypt, 81, 83 and 85 Centre street, comprising many desirable Books exhumed in moving.　To be sold at Auction on Tuesday and Wednesday, Nov. 24 and 25, 1863, etc.　8°, pp. 28.
　1,000 copies.

HALL, JAMES.　Notice of some new Species of Fossils from a Locality of the Niagara Group, in Indiana; with a List of Identified Species from the same Place.　8°, pp. 24.

HALLIWELL, JAMES ORCHARD.　An Historical Sketch of the Provincial Dialects of England, illustrated by numerous Examples.　8°, pp. 126.
　150 copies.

[HEMINGWAY, A. M., compiler.]　Songs of the War.　12°, pp. 96.
　1,000 copies.

HOMES, HENRY A.　Observations on the Design and Import of Medals. 8°, pp. 8.

HOUGH, G. W.　Description of a New Cataloguing and Charting Machine. 8°, pp. 11.
　200 copies. Engravings.

HYMNS for State Street Presbyterian Sabbath School, 1863.　16°, pp. 58.
　500 copies.

LAST WILL and Testament of Blandina Dudley of Albany, N. Y.　8°, pp. 8.

LAWYER, JOHN D.　Our Country; its Peace, Prosperity, and Perpetuity: a Thanksgiving Sermon preached in Coeymans, Albany County, N. Y. on Thursday, Nov. 27, 1862.　8°, pp. 24.
　500 copies.

LEWIS.　Annual Address before the Historic-Genealogical Society.　8°.
　500 copies.

LINTNER, GEORGE A.　A Historical Discourse delivered before the Schoharie County Bible Society, at its Semi-Centennial Meeting, in the Lutheran Church, Schoharie, Oct. 6, 1863.　8°, pp. 29.

MEMOIR of Richard Marvin Strong, a Member of the Albany Bar, and Adjutant of the 177th Regiment N. Y. Volunteers, who died at Bonnet Carré, La., May 12, 1863.　8°, pp. 45.
　400 copies.

MEMOIR of S. G. Drake.   8°, pp. 36.
  100 copies.

MEMORIAL of George Van Santvoord.   8°, pp. 53.
  300 copies with portrait.

MEMORIAL of Hamlet H. Hickcox, born at Lanesborough, Mass., Sept. 6,
  1790; died at Albany, N. Y., Feb. 9, 1863.   8°, pp. 23.

MESSINGER, GEORGE W. Genealogy of the Messinger Family. 8°, pp. 14.
  50 copies.

MINUTES of the Particular Synod of Albany.   8°, pp. 64.
  400 copies.

MINUTES of the Sixty-eighth Synod of the Evangelical Lutheran Ministerium of the State of New York and Adjacent States and Countries,
  held in the Evan. Lutheran Church, Germantown, Columbia County,
  N. Y., commencing on Saturday, Sept. 5, and ending Wednesday, Sept.
  9, 1863. 8°, pp. 58.
  750 copies.

MINUTES of the Thirty-third Annual Convention of the Hartwick Synod,
  of the Evangelical Lutheran Church in the State of New York, held at
  Canajoharie, Montgomery County, N. Y., Sept. 25–30, 1863. 8°, pp. 44.
  1,000 copies.

MINUTES of the Twenty-ninth Anniversary of the Washington Union
  Baptist Association, held with the Battskill Baptist Church at Union
  Village, commencing Tuesday, June 2d, 1863. 8°, pp. 17.
  1,000 copies.

MINUTES of the Washington County Supervisors. 8°.
  3,000 copies.

MOTTOES of the Second Reformed Protestant Dutch Church. 8°, pp. 16.
  500 copies.

MUNSELL, JOEL. Webster's Calendar, or the Albany Almanac, for the
  year of our Lord 1864. 12°, pp. 36.

MURRAY, DAVID. A Plan for a Park for the City of Albany. 8°, pp. 16.
  Map.

NEILL, EDWARD D. Biographical Sketch of Dr. Jonathan Potts, Director
  General of the Hospitals of the Northern and Middle Departments in
  the War of the Revolution, with Extracts from his Correspondence.
  8°, pp. 18.

NEMO, MRS. [Miss M. E. Roberts.] A Series of Appeals, or Lectures
  addressed not behind a Curtain to one unfortunate Man, but to all Men
  and their Families — a Woman's apology for appearing in Public — an
  Appeal in behalf of unmarried Women — Unwomanly Women, and
  Unmanly Men — Our Present War and Woman's Relation to it. 12°.
  1,000 copies.

PALMER, RAY. The Opening Future ; or the Results of the Present War.
  A Thanksgiving Discourse, Nov. 26, 1863. 8°, pp. 28.
  500 copies.

PROCEEDINGS of the Fiftieth Anniversary of the Washington County Bible Society, and other Anniversaries of Benevolent Associations, held at Salem, N. Y., Sept. 4th, 1862. 12°, pp. 36.
　1,000 copies.

PROCEEDINGS of the Fifty-first Anniversary of the Washington County Bible Society, and other Anniversaries of Benevolent Associations, held at Argyle, N. Y., Sept. 5th, 1863. 12°, pp. 26.
　1,000 copies.

[RAWSON, T. R.] Twentieth Annual Report of the Albany City Missionary Society, presented June 6th, 1863. 12°, pp. 12.
　100 copies.

REED and CADWALLADER. Reprint of the Reed and Cadwallader Pamphlets; with an Appendix. 8°, pp. iv, 82, 44, 12.
　200 copies. Spicy correspondence between Joseph B. Reed and J. Remmington and Son.

REPORT of the Forty ninth Annual Examination of the Albany Female Academy, presented at their Anniversary, Tuesday, June 16, 1863. 8°, pp. 20.
　1,000 copies.

REPORT of the Ninth Annual Examination of Mrs. Loveridge's School, and the Commencement Exercises on their Ninth (etc.) Anniversary. 8°.

REPORT of the Treasurer of Union College. 8°, pp.
　50 copies.

RUDO ENSAYO, tentativa de una Prevencional Descripcion Geographica de la Provincia de Sonora, sus Terminos y Confines; ó mejor, Coleccion de Materiales para hacerla quien lo supiere Mejor ; compilada así de Noticias adquiridas por el Colector en sus Viajes por casi toda ella, como Subministradas por los Padres Missioneros y Practicos de la Teirra: dirigida al Remedio de ella, por un Amigo del Bien Comun. 4°, pp. x, 208.

SâGEAN, MATHIEU. Extrait de la, Relation des Avantures et Voyage de Mathieu Sâgean. 8°, pp 32.
　160 copies.

ST. STEPHEN's College Catalogue. 8°, pp. 16.
　500 copies.

SECOND Bulletin of the Chemical Society of Union College. 12°, pp. 12.
　400 copies.

SHEPPARD, JOHN H. Brief Memoir of Dr. Winslow Lewis. 8°, pp. 33.
　100 copies. Portrait.

SIXTH Annual Meeting of the Albany Young Men's Christian Association, held Monday Evening, March 23, 1863, in the Pearl Street Baptist Church, Albany, N. Y. 8°, pp. 23.
　1,300 copies.

SKETCH of the Family of Dumaresq, to which are added Reminiscences of James Dumaresq, and an Appendix of Documents.   8°, pp. 23.
100 copies.

SMITH, AUGUSTUS.   Catalogue of the Teachers' Institute in the Second District of Schoharie County, held at Cobleskill, N. Y., commencing Oct. 20 and ending Oct. 31, 1862.   8°, pp. 20.

SPRAGUE, W. B.   Sermon on the Death of Mrs. H. N. Pohlman. 8°, pp. 18.
500 copies.

STATE Street Presbyterian Church, Albany, N. Y. Covenant and Membership.   8°, pp. 16, 14.

STRONG, R. M., Sermon on Death of.   8°, pp. 34.
350 copies.

SUNDAY School Hymns of the Broadway M. E. Sunday School.   16°, pp. 45.

SWINBURNE, JOHN, and Willard S. D.   Relief of Sick and Wounded Soldiers.   8°, pp. 8.

THE Troy Directory, for the year 1863 : including Lansingburgh, West Troy and Green Island; also, a Business Directory, a Record of the City Government, its Institutions, &c.   12°, pp. 36, 431.
850 copies.

TOWNSEND, HOWARD.   The Sunbeam and the Spectrascope.   8°, pp. 15.
150 copies.   Reprinted under title of The Sunbeam and the Spectroscope.

TRASK, WILLIAM B.   A Brief Memoir of Andrew Henshaw Ward.   8°, pp. 11.
2 Portraits.

TWENTY-SEVENTH Annual Report of the Albany City Tract and Missionary Society, presented at the Annual Meeting in the North Dutch Church, December 21, 1862.   8°, pp. 22.
1,000 copies.

UNION College Catalogue.   8°, pp. 48.
600 copies.

UNION College Magazine.   8°.
200 copies.   Several numbers.

VAN HORNE, DAVID.   Sermon.   8°, pp. 16.
350 copies.

VASSAL Genealogy.   8°, pp. 32.
400 copies.

Vocabulario San Antonio.   8°, pp. 72.
160 copies ; and 10 large.

WALLACE, JOHN WILLIAM. An Address delivered at the Celebration by the New York Historical Society, May 20, 1863, of the Two Hundredth Birth Day of Mr. William Bradford, who introduced the Art of Printing into the Middle Colonies, of British America. Published with an Introductory Note, in Pursuance of a Resolution of the New York Historical Society, parts omitted in the delivery being now inserted. 8°, pp. 114.
750 copies. Plates.

WASHINGTON Directory. 8°, pp. 312.
1,200 copies.

WATSON, WINSLOW C. Pioneer History of the Champlain Valley ; being an Account of the Settlement of the Town of Willsborough by William Gilliland, together with his Journal and other Papers, and a Memoir, and Historical and Illustrative Notes. 8°, pp. 231.

WATSON, WINSLOW C. The Life and Character of the Hon. Richard Skinner; a Discourse read before, and at the request of, the Vermont Historical Society, at Montpelier, Oct. 20, 1863. 8°, pp. 30.

WINSLOW LEWIS. Annual Address of the President of the New England Historic-Genealogical Society, delivered Jan. 7, 1863. 8°, pp. 18.

ZABRISKIE, F. N. Weighed in the Balance ; a Fast Day Sermon, preached in the Second Reformed Dutch Church of Coxsackie, Thursday Morning, April 30, 1863. 12°, pp. 26.
200 copies.

1864.

AMES, CHARLES G. Dead Flies in Precious Ointment; a Discourse on Morals in America; delivered in the Unitarian Church in Albany, N. Y., Sunday, July 3, 1864. 8°, pp. 16.

ANNUAL Catalogue of the Officers and Students of Hartwick Theological and Classical Seminary, for the Academic year ending Aug. 24, 1864. 8°, pp. 12.
300 copies.

ANNUAL Report of the Treasurer of Union College, made June 30, 1864. 8°, pp. 22.
50 copies.

ARTICLES of Association and By-Laws of the Albany City Salt Manufacturing Company of the State of Michigan, organized Sept. 1, 1864, under the General Mining and Manufacturing Law of the State of Michigan. 8°, pp. 19.
100 copies.

BARNES, WILLIAM. The Settlement and Early History of Albany. 8°, pp. 100.
300 copies.

BAYLIES, FRANCIS.   Some Remarks on the Life and Character of General David Cobb, delivered at the Taunton Lyceum, July 2, 1830. 8°, pp. 18.
Portrait.

BOYD, ANDREW.   Boyd's Washington and Georgetown Directory, containing also a Business Directory of Washington, Georgetown and Alexandria, to which is prefixed a Guide, etc. 8°, pp. 370.
Map.

BROWN, S. D.   The Bible, the Source of True Civilization; a Sermon preached at the Fifty-third Anniversary of the Albany County Bible Society, Feb. 24, 1864. 8°, pp. 34.

BURIAL of Mechanics at Union College. 8°, pp. 30.

CASES in the Supreme Court of the State of New York. 8°.
12 copies.

CASWELL, ALEXIS.   A Brief Memoir of John Barstow, of Providence, R. I. 8°, pp. 11.
100 copies.   Portrait.

CATALOGUE and Circular of Albany Medical College. 8°, pp. 16.
5,000 copies.

CATALOGUE of Broadway Methodist Episcopal Sunday School. 16°, pp. 24.
150 copies.

CATALOGUE of Cottage Hill Seminary, Poughkeepsie. 8°, pp. 15.
500 copies.

CATALOGUE of Rare, Curious and Useful Books, and Tracts, chiefly Historical (relating principally to New England) which have been collected during several years, and are now offered for sale at the prices annexed.   For Sale by S. G. Drake, at his office, No. 13 Bromfield Street, up stairs, Boston.   Square 8°, pp. 44.
350 copies.

CATALOGUE of the Assets of the National Bank to be sold by James, Receiver, at the Room of the Board of Trade, 465 Broadway, Albany, on Tuesday, Jan. 5, 1864, at 11 o'clock, A. M. 8°, pp. 8.

CATALOGUE of the Library of the State Street Presbyterian Church Sabbath School. 16°, pp. 29.
200 copies.

CATALOGUE of the Pearl Street Baptist Sabbath School Library. 16°, pp. 16.
300 copies.

CATALOGUE of the Third Presbyterian Sabbath School. 16°, pp. 32.
200 copies.

CATALOGUE of the Young Ladies' Association. 8°.
150 copies.

CIRCULAR and Catalogue of the Albany Female Academy.   Founded A. D. 1814.   Incorporated Feb. 16, 1821. 8°, pp. 19.
1,000 copies.

CIRCULAR and Catalogue of Union College, Sixty-ninth year, Third Term. 8°, pp. 48.
1,000 copies.

COHOES School District Library Catalogue. 8°, pp. 40.
800 copies.

[COLVIN & BINGHAM.] Slavery, or Involuntary Servitude: does it Legally Exist in the State of New York? Points on Argument in Court of Appeals, Opinions in Court of Appeals. 8°, pp. 60.
2,600 copies.

CONSTITUTION and By-Laws of the Albany Dental Association. 8°, pp. 8.
250 copies.

CONSTITUTION, By-Laws and Rules of Order of Hudson River Engine Company No. 1, of the Village of Coxsackie. 16°, pp. 15.

CRUIKSHANK, JAMES. The New York Teacher; a Monthly Journal of School and Home Education. Vol. XIII. 8°, pp. iv, 423.
1,550 copies.

CUSHMAN. Funeral Sermon on the Death of Mrs. Cushman. 8°, pp. 16.
150 copies.

DEANE, W. R. A Biographical Sketch of Elkanah Watson, Founder of Agricultural Societies in America, and the Projector of Canal Communication in New York State, with a Brief Genealogy of the Watson Family, early settled in Plymouth Colony. 8°, pp. 16.
100 copies. Portrait.

DEFENCE of Stonington (Connecticut) against a British Squadron, August 9th to 12th, 1814. Square 8°, pp. 54.
100 copies; 6 large (?) Collected and arranged by J. Hammond Trumbull of Hartford.

DEVOL, CHARLES. Sermon. 8°, pp. 34.
500 copies.

DURRIE, DANIEL S. Genealogical History of the Holt Family in the United States; More particularly the Descendants of Nicholas Holt of Newbury and Andover, Mass., 1634–1644, and of William Holt of New Haven, Conn. 8°, pp. iv, 367.
300 copies.

EPISTOLA Rev. Gabrielis Dreuilléttes Societatis Jesu Presbyteri, ad Dominum Illustrissimum, Dominum Joannem Winthrop, Scutarium. Small 8°, pp. 16.
This work though dated 1864, was completed in 1866, having been about eighteen months *in the press.*

EXTRACTS from the Doep Book, or Baptismal Register of the Reformed Protestant Dutch Church of Schenectady, N. Y. 8°, pp. 14.

FIFTY-THIRD Annual Report of the Albany County Bible Society, organized A. D. 1810. 8°, pp. 15.

FOURTEENTH Annual Catalogue of the Sans Souci Seminary, Ballston Spa, Saratoga Co., N. Y. 8°, pp. 12.
516 copies.

GEORGE, W. C. Medical Notice. 8°, pp. 8.

GILMAN ARTHUR, of Glynllyn. Genealogy of the Gilman Family in England and America : traced in the Line of the Hon. John Gilman, of Exeter, N. H. Square 8°, pp. 23, il.
> 30 copies. Portrait of C. R. Gilman.

GOWANS, W. Catalogue of Books. 8°, pp. 32.
> 800 copies.

HARSHA, DAVID A. Life of Philip Doddridge, D.D., with Notices of some of his Cotemporaries, and Specimens of his Style. 8°, pp. 249.
> 25 copies large paper. Portrait of Doddridge.

HOUGH, FRANKLIN B. History of Duryée's Brigade, during the Campaign in Virginia under Gen. Pope, and in Maryland under Gen. McClellan, in the Summer and Autumn of 1862. 8°, pp. 200.
> 400 copies. Portrait of Duryée.

[HOUGH, G. W.] Report of the Astronomer in charge of the Dudley Observatory, for the year 1863. 8°, pp. 43.
> 500 copies.

HYMNS for State Street Presbyterian Sabbath School, 1864. 16°, pp. 106.
> 1,000 copies.

HYMNS for the Broadway M. E. Sabbath School. 16°, pp. 45.
> Two editions of 500 copies each.

IN MEMORIAM : Helen Louisa Parmelee, born Feb. 15, 1821 ; died Nov. 27, 1863. 8°, pp. 15.

JEWELL, FREDERICK S. The Nature and Cause of Regeneration; a Sermon. 8°, pp. 22.
> 100 copies.

LEWIS, TAYLER. State Rights : A Photograph from the Ruins of Ancient Greece. 12°, pp. 96.
> 750 copies.

LOMBARD Family. 8°, pp. 2.
> 100 copies.

MANUAL of the Regents of the University of the State of New York, 1864. 12°, pp. xvi, 200.
> 1,000 copies.

MATHER, INCREASE. Early History of New England : being a Relation of Hostile Passages between the Indians and European Voyagers and First Settlers ; and a full Narrative of Hostilities, to the close of the War with the Pequots, in the year 1637 ; also a detailed Account of the Origin of the War with King Philip. With an Introduction and Notes by Samuel G. Drake. Square 8°, pp. 309.
> 250 copies ; 20 large.

MEMOIR of John Allan. Royal 8°, pp. 39.
> 80 copies. Written by Evert A. Duyckinck. Portrait of John Allan.

MEMORIAL of Mrs. Augusta Matilda Irwin, who died Nov. 7th, 1863. 8°, pp. 54.
> 300 copies.

MILET, PIERRE. Relation de sa Captivité parmi les Onneouts en 1690–1, par le R. P. Pierre Milet de la Compagnie de Jésus. Small 8°, pp. 56,
160 copies.

MINUTES of the Particular Synod of Albany. 8°, pp. 38.
400 copies.

MINUTES of the Sixty-eighth Anniversary of the Rennsselaerville Association, held with the Baptist Church of Westerlo, Albany County, N. Y. Sept. 7 and 8, 1864. 8°, pp. 16.
700 copies.

MINUTES of the Sixty-ninth Synod of the Evangelical Lutheran Ministerium of the State of New York and adjacent States and Countries, held in Zion's German Lutheran Church, Utica, N. Y., from Saturday, Sept. 3, to Thursday, Sept. 8, 1864. 8°, pp. 68.
500 copies.

MINUTES of the Thirtieth Anniversary of the Washington Union Baptist Association, held with the First Fort Ann Church at Comstock's Landing, commencing Tuesday, June 7, 1864. 8°, pp. 18.
500 copies.

MINUTES of the Thirty-fourth Annual Convention of the Hartwick Synod of the Evangelical Lutheran Church in the State of New York, held at Livingston, Columbia County, N. Y., Sept. 9–15, 1864. 8°, pp. 48.
500 copies.

MUNSELL, JOEL. A Chronology of Paper and Paper-Making. Third Edition. 8°, pp. 174.

MUNSELL, JOEL. Webster's Calendar, or the Albany Almanac for the year of our Lord 1865. 12°, pp. 36.

NEW YORK State Business Directory for 1864, by Adams, Sampson & Co. 8°, pp. 792.
4,000 copies.

OLD Church at Quincy, Mass. 8°, pp. 17.
200 copies

ONE Hundred and Tenth Annual Catalogue of the Officers and Students of Columbia College for 1863–1864. 8°, pp. 119.
400 copies.

OPERATIONS of the French Fleet under the Count de Grasse in 1781–2, as described in two Contemporaneous Journals. Royal 8°, pp. 16.
150 copies. Edited by John G. Shea.

POINTS in the Court of Appeals of the State of New York. 8°.
20 copies.

POINTS in the Supreme Court of the State of New York. 8°.
12 copies.

PROCEEDINGS of the Fifty-second Anniversary of the Washington County Bible Society, and other Anniversaries of Benevolent Associations, held at West Hebron, N. Y., Sept. 7th, 1864. 12°, pp. 28.
1,000 copies.

PROCESS Verbal. [E. A. Duyckinck.] 8°, pp. 15.
35 copies.

RECORDS of Salem Witchcraft, copied from the original Documents. 2 vols. Square 8°, pp. 279, 287.
200 copies.

REPORT of the Fiftieth Annual Examination of the Albany Female Academy, presented at their Anniversary, Tuesday, June 14, 1864. 8°, pp. 20.
1,000 copies.

REPORT of the Standing Committee of the Divinity School of the Protestant Episcopal Church, Philadelphia, June, 1864. 12°, pp. 23.
2,500 copies.

ROXBURY Directory, containing the City Record, the Names of the Citizens, and a Business Directory, with an Almanac for 1864. 16°, pp. 282, 84.
750 copies. Map.

SCHOOL of Mines, Columbia College, 1863–64. 8°, pp. 8.

SERMON on the Death of Mrs. Patten. 8°, pp. 32.
400 copies.

SHEA, JOHN GILMARY. The Historical Magazine, and Notes and Queries concerning the Antiquities, History and Biography of America. Vol. VIII–IX (July 1864 to May, 1865.)
1,100 copies.

SIXTH Annual Catalogue of the Officers and Students of the Law School of Columbia College, for 1863–1864. 8°, pp. 40.
1,000 copies.

SIXTH Annual Report of the Windham Association, Consociation and Benevolent Association, with Statistics of 1864 for the Churches. 8°, pp. 8.
1,400 copies.

STATUTEN des Allgemeinen Deutschen Frauen-Vereins zu Albany, Gegründet den 14 Februar, 1864. 16°, pp. 4.

STONE, WILLIAM L. The Poetry and History of Wyoming: containing Campbell's Gertrude, and the History of Wyoming from its Discovery to the Beginning of the Present Century. Third Edition, with an Index. 12°, pp. xiii, 406.
Edition of 1844, with new title and Index.

THIRD Annual Report of the Trade and Commerce of the City of Albany for the year 1863. 8°, pp. 50.
300 copies. These reports were compiled by Wm. Lacy.

TONGIORGI. Institutiones Philosophicæ Salvatoris Tongiorgi E. Societate Iesu ab eodem in Compendium Redactæ. 8°, pp. 328.
500 copies.

TOWNSEND, HOWARD. The Spectroscope. 8°, pp. 15.
300 copies, 2d edition.

TRANSACTIONS of the Albany Institute. Vol. IV. 8°, pp. 323.
250 copies.

TROY Directory. 8°, pp. 158.
1,000 copies.

TWOMBLY, A. S. Thanksgiving Plea for Free Labor, North and South. 8°, pp. 30.
200 copies.

UNION College Memorials. 8°, pp. 10.
400 copies.

VICKERS Family. 8°, pp. 3.
100 copies.

WALWORTH, REUBEN HYDE. Hyde Genealogy: or the Descendants in the Female as well as in the Male Lines from William Hyde of Norwich, with their Places of Residence, and Dates of Births, Marriages, &c., and other Particulars of them and their Families and Ancestry. 2 vols., 8°, pp. viii, 1446.
375 copies. 22 portraits.

WHITMORE, WILLIAM A. Notes on the Winthrop Family, and its English connections before the Emigration to New England. 8°, pp. 6.
100 copies.

WILLARD, SYLVESTER D. Annals of the Medical Society of the County of Albany, 1866–1851, with Biographical Sketches of Deceased Members. 8°, pp. 368.
300 copies. 4 portraits.

WILSON, J. Phrasis; a Treatise on the History and Structure of the Different Languages of the World, with a comparative View of the Forms of their Words, and the Style of their Expressions. 8°, pp. 384.
300 copies. Photograph of author.

1865.

AN Account of Abimilech Coody and other Celebrated Writers of New York; in a Letter from a Traveller to his Friend in South Carolina; January 1815. Royal 8°, pp. 22.
Edited by Evert A. Duyckinck.

ANNUAL Report of the Treasurer of Union College, made June 30, 1865. 8°, pp. 20.
50 copies.

BIGOT, JACQUES. Relation de la Mission Abnaquise de St. Francois de Sales l'année 1702. Par le Père Jacques Bigot, de la Compagnie de Jésus. Small 8°, pp. 26.

BLADENSBURG RACES. Written shortly after the Capture of Washington City, August 24, 1814. 4to, pp. 16.
75 copies.

BLEEKER, LEONARD. Order Book of Captain Leonard Bleeker, Major of
Brigade in the Early Part of the Expedition under Gen. James Clinton,
against the Indian Settlements of Western New York, in the Campaign of 1779. Square 8°, pp. 138.
250 copies ; 50 large paper.

BOUDRYE, LOUIS N. Historic Records of the Fifth New York Cavalry,
First Ira Harris Guard ; its Organization, Marches, Raids, Scouts,
Engagements and General Services, during the Rebellion of 1861–1865,
with Observations of the Author by the way, giving Sketches of the
Armies of the Potomac and of the Shenandoah. Also, interesting
Accounts of Prison Life and of the Secret Service. Complete Lists of
its, Officers and Men. By Rev. Louis N. Boudrye, Chaplain of the
Regiment. 12°, pp. 358.
Portraits and plates.

BULLETIN of the Class of '62 of Union College. 8°, pp. 15.

BYFIELD, NATHANIEL. An Account of the Late Revolution in New England. Square 8°, pp. 27.
200 copies small ; 50 large paper.

BY-LAWS, Rules and Regulations of the Evergreen Cemetery Association,
of Salem, N. Y. 8°, pp. 20.
1,000 copies.

CASES in the Court of Appeals of the State of New York. 8°.
20 copies.

CATALOGUE and Circular of the Albany Medical College. 8°, pp. 16.
4,000 copies.

CATALOGUE of a Private Collection of Books, including English Editions
of Theological Works, Pamphlets, etc., etc., to be sold at Auction on
Friday Evening, Nov. 24, 1865, etc. 8°, pp. 11.
250 copies.

CATALOGUE of Dr. Mason F. Cogswell's Library. 8°, pp. 32.
400 copies.

CATALOGUE of the Law School. 8°, pp. 16.
6,000 copies.

CATALOGUE of the Officers and Students of Union College. 8°, pp. 48.
600 copies.

CATALOGUE of the Second R. P. Dutch Church Library. 16°, pp. 36.
400 copies.

CATALOGUE of the Washington Avenue Sunday School Library. 16°, pp. 20.
250 copies.

CERTAIN Inducements to Well-Minded People who are here Straitned in
their Estates or otherwise ; or, such as are willing, out of Noble and
Publike Principles, to transport themselves or some Servants, or Agents
for them into the West Indies, for the Propagating of the Gospel and
Increase of Trade. Square 8°, pp. 24.
250 copies ; 50 large paper.

CHARTER and By-Laws of the Young Men's Association for Mutual Improvement, in the City of Albany. By-Laws adopted by Executive Committee April 14, 1859, as amended up to December 1, 1865. 16°, pp. 26.
250 copies.

CIRCULAR and Catalogue of the Albany Female Academy. Founded A.D. 1814. Incorporated Feb. 16, 1821. 8°, pp. 19.
1,000 copies.

CLARK, JAMES H. The Iron Hearted Regiment; Being an Account of the Battles, Marches and Gallant Deeds performed by the 115th Regiment, N. Y. Vols. Also a List of the Dead and Wounded; an Account of Hundreds of Brave Men Shot on a Score of hard-fought Fields of Strife; A Complete Statement of Harper's Ferry Surrender; Sketches of the Officers: A History of the Flags, and those who bore them, together with Touching Incidents, Thrilling Adventures, Amusing Scenes, etc., etc., etc. 12°, pp. xii, 337.
1,000 copies.

COLUMBUS'S Letter. 8°, pp. 12.
75 copies.

CONSTITUTION Chrystal Fount, &c. 8°, pp. 24.
200 copies. Done for Mr. Heaton, printer at Gloversville.

COOK, EBEN. The Sot Weed Factor: or, a Voyage to Maryland, A Satyr in which is described the Laws, Government, Courts and Constitutions of the Country, and also the Buildings, Feats, Froliks, Entertainments and Drunken Humours of the Inhabitants of that Part of America. In Burlesque Verse. Square 8°, pp. vi. 27.
150 copies; 34 large paper.

CRUIKSHANK, JAMES, LL. D. The New York Teacher; a Monthly Journal of School and Home Education. Vol. XIV, 8°, pp. 384.
2,000 copies.

DAY BREAKING if not the Sun Rising of the Gospel with the Indians in New England. Square 8°, pp. iv, 32.
250 copies; 50 large paper.

DECLARATION by the Representatives of the United Colonies of North America, now met in General Congress at Philadelphia, setting forth the Causes and Necessity of their taking up Arms. 4to, pp. 13.
75 copies; 10 on drawing paper.

ELIOT'S Catechism. Square 8°, pp. 5.

FIFTY-FOURTH Annual Report of the Albany County Bible Society. Organized A. D. 1810. 8°, pp. 16.

[FROTHINGHAM, Rev. W.] Zoe, or the Martel Papers, a Manuscript of the Conciergerie. 12°, pp. 468.
1,000 copies. Portraits and plates.

FURTHER Manifestation of the Progress of the Gospel, among the Indians in New England. Square 8°, pp. xii, 21.
250 copies; 50 large paper..

GOWANS, W.   Catalogue of Books.   8°, pp. 44.
700 copies.

[GOWANS, W.]   A Catalogue of the Library and Antiquarian Collection
of John Allan, Esq., with the Names of Purchasers and the Price each
Article sold for, prefaced by a few Introductory Remarks.   8°, pp. 70.
400 copies.

[HALL, BENJAMIN H.]   A Tribute of Respect by the Citizens of Troy, to
the Memory of Abraham Lincoln.   8°, pp. xl, 342.
500 copies ; 50 large paper.

HALL, BENJAMIN H.   History of Eastern Vermont, from its Earliest Set-
lement to the close of the Eighteenth Century, with a Biographical
Chapter and Appendixes.   Sup. Roy. 8°, 2 vols.
50 copies ; large paper copy. Fac simile of inquest, and wood cuts.

HARSHA, D. A.   Life of Philip Doddridge, D.D., with Notices of some of
his Cotemporaries, and Specimens of his Style.   8°, pp. 249.
250 copies. Portrait and plate.

HARSHA, D. A.   Life of the Rev. James Hervey.   Royal 8°, pp. 58.

HATHAWAY, W.   Minutes of the Forty-seventh Annual Session of the N. Y.
Eastern Conference, held at Freehold, Greene County, N. Y., June 1st,
2d and 3d, 1865, together with the Annual Address.   12°, pp. 37.

HATHAWAY, WARREN.   The Church and the Times ; Annual Address de-
liveredbefore the New York Eastern Christian Conference, on Thursday,
June 1, 1865, at its Forty-seventh Session held at Freehold, Greene Co.,
N. Y.   8°, pp. 23.
550 copies.

HAWLEY.   Sermon.   8°, pp. 20.
500 copies.

HOMES, HENRY A.   Observations on the Design and Import of Medals.
8°, pp. 16.
62 copies.

HOUGH, FRANKLIN B.   Bibliographical List of Books and Pamphlets containing Eulogies, Orations, Poems, or other Papers, relating to the
Death of General Washington, or to the Honors paid to his Memory.
8°, pp. 59.
25 copies.

HOUGH, FRANKLIN B.   Washingtoniana ; or, Memorials of the Death of
George Washington, giving an Account of the Funeral Honors paid
to his Memory, with a list of Tracts and Volumes printed upon the
Occasion, and a Catalogue of Medal s commemorating the Event. 2 vols.,
Royal 8°, pp. 272, 304.
200 copies ; 90 large paper. Drawing paper. Also two portraits of Washington.

HOUGH, G. W.   Description of an Automatic Registering and Printing
Barometer.   8°, pp. 22.
500 copies. Engravings.

HUBBARD, REV. WILLIAM. The History of the Indian Wars in New England from the first Settlement to the Termination of the War with King Philip, in 1677. From the Original Work, Carefully Revised, and accompanied with an Historical Preface, Life and Pedigree of the Author, and Extensive Notes, by Samuel G. Drake. 2 vols., square 8°, pp. xxxii, 292, 303.
   300 copies ; 50 large paper. Ancient map.

JENNINGS, PAUL. A Colored Man's Reminiscences of James Madison. 4to, pp. 21.
   75 copies.

KNIGHT, MADAM. Private Journal of a Journey from Boston to New York in the year 1704, kept by Madam Knight. Square 8°, pp. 92.
   250 copies ; 50 large paper. Edited by Wm. L. Learned.

LANSING House, and Pruyn House. 8°, pp. 5.
   Plates.

LAPE, T. Sermon on the Death of Rev. Heller. 8°, pp. 8.
   450 copies.

LAW Catalogue. 8°, pp. 40.
   1,000 copies.

LIGHT appearing more and more towards the Perfect Day : or a farther Discovery of the present State of the Indians in New England, concerning the Progress of the Gospel amongst them, manifested by Letters from such as preacht to them there. Published by Henry Whitefield, late Pastor of the Church of Christ, Gilford in New England, who came late thence. London, 1651. Square 8°, pp. viii, 46.
   200 copies ; 50 large paper.

MEMOIR of Otis Allen, with the Proceedings of the Albany Bar, and of other Public Bodies, with the Sermon of his Pastor, the Rev. Henry Darling, D. D. 8°, pp. 54.

MEMORIAL of the Golden Wedding of Leonard and Jenette Hodgman, at Stillwater, N. Y., Jan. 12, 1865. 8°, pp. 14.

MINUTES of a Conspiracy against the Liberties of America. 4to, pp. xiv, iv, 114.
   150 copies ; 75 4to large ; 25 folio. Edited by W. A. Whiteman.

MINUTES of a Court of Inquiry, upon the Case of Major John Andrè, with accompanying Documents, published in 1780, by order of Congress, with Additional Appendix, containing copies of the Papers found upon Major Andrè when arrested, and other Documents relating to the subject. Square 8°, pp. iv, 66.
   100 copies. Portrait of Major Andrè.

MINUTES of the Particular Synod of Albany, convened in Regular Session. 8°.
   400 copies.

MINUTES of the Seventieth Synod of the Evangelical Lutheran Ministerium of the State of New York and Adjacent States and Countries held in St Luke's Church, Valatie, N. Y., from Saturday, Sept. 2, to Thursday, Sept. 7, 1865. 8°, pp. 52.
600 copies.

MUNSELL, JOEL. A Chronology of Paper and Paper-Making. 8°, pp. 172.
200 copies.

MUNSELL, JOEL. Collections on the History of Albany, from its Discovery to the Present Time, with Notices of its Public Institutions, and Biographical Sketches of Citizens Deceased. Vol. I. Royal 8°, pp. viii, 529.
200 copies. Plates.

MUNSELL, JOEL. List of Ancient and Modern Books, New and Second Hand, offered at the Net Prices affixed, by J. Munsell, No. 78 State Street, Albany, N. Y., for cash. 12°, pp. 36.

MUNSELL, JOEL. Valuable Private Library; Catalogue of a Rare and extensive Collection of Books principally relating to America, comprising a portion of the Private Library of Joel Munsell of Albany, N. Y., to be sold at Auction April 11, 1865, and the following Days, by J. E. Cooley. 8°, pp. 123.
500 copies ; 50 large paper.

MUNSELL, JOEL. Webster's Calendar, or the Albany Almanac, for the year of our Lord 1866. 12°, pp. 36.

MURPHY, HENRY C. Anthology of New Netherland, or Transactions from the early Dutch Poets of New York, with Memoirs of their Lives. Royal 8°, pp. 209.
155 copies. Portrait of Steendam.

NASON, ELIAS. Sir Charles Henry Frankland, Baronet; or Boston in Colonial Times. 8°, pp. 129.
250 copies ; 50 large.

NEW ENGLAND'S First Fruits: with Divers other Special Matters concerning that Country. Square 8°, pp. iv, 47.
250 copies; 50 large paper.

NEWS from New England, 1676. 4to, pp. 22.
65 copies. Printed for W. E. Woodward.

O'CALLAGHAN, E. B., LL. D. The Register of New Netherland; 1626 to 1674. Royal 8°, pp. xx, 198.
200 copies.

PALMER, RAY. Hymns and Sacred Pieces, with Miscellaneous Poems. 8°, pp. 195.
25 copies. Was stereotyped and afterwards printed in 12mo.

PALMER, RAY. Reminiscences of our Work for Fifteen Years; a Discourse delivered in the First Congregational Church, Albany, on Sabbath Morning, Dec. 24, 1865. 8°, pp. 30.
250 copies.

PATTERN List of Townsend's Furnace and Machine Shop, Albany, N. Y., comprising a Catalogue of the Wheel and Pulley Patterns, and Racks, and Roll chills belonging to that Establishment. 5th Edition. 12° pp. 103.
2,000 copies.

PHILLIPS, HENRY, JR. Historical Sketches of the Paper Currency of the American Colonies, prior to the Adoption of the Federal Constitution. First Series, Continental Paper Money. Historical Sketches of American Paper Currency, Second Series. 2 vols., square 8°, pp. 233, 264.
300 copies; 20 large paper.

POETICAL Epistle to his Excellency George Washington, Esq., Commander in Chief of the Armies of the United States of America, from an Inhabitant of the State of Maryland; to which is annexed a short Sketch of General Washington's Life and Character. Annapolis: Printed 1779; London reprinted 1780. Square 8°, pp. 24.
75 copies large paper.

POINTS in the Court of Appeals of the State of New York. 8°.
20 copies.

POINTS in the Supreme Court of the State of New York. 8°.
12 copies.

PROCEEDINGS of a General Court Martial for the Trial of Major General Arnold; with an Introduction, Notes, and Index. 8°, pp. xxix, 182.
145 copies. Portrait of Arnold.

PROCEEDINGS of the Bar of the County of Clinton, New York, with other Memorials, commemorative of the Life and Character of William Swetland. 8°, pp. 53.
200 copies.

PROCEEDINGS of the Board of Supervisors of Washington County, November and December Sessions, 1864. 8°, pp. 25.
3,500 copies.

PROCEEDINGS of the Hamilton County Teachers' Institute, organized at the Public School House at Wells, on Tuesday, Oct. 25, 1864. 8°, pp. 12.
75 copies.

PROCESS Verbal of the Ceremony of Installation of President of the New York Historical Society, as it will be performed February 8, 1820. 8°, pp. 15.
25 copies.

PUBLICATIONS of the Prince Society, established May 25th, 1858. The Hutchinson Papers. 2 vols., square 8°, pp. xv, title, ii, 324.
150 copies; 10 large paper. Vol. I edited by William H. Whitmore. Vol. II edited by William S. Appleton.

RELATIONS des Affaires du Canada, en 1696, et des Missions des Péres de la Compagnie de Jésus jusqu'en 1702. Small 8°, pp. 42.

RELATION des Affaires du Canada, en 1696, avec des Lettres des Pères de la Compagnie de Jésus de puis 1696 jusqu'en 1702. Small 8°, pp. 73.
  This was a second edition with additions.

RELATION of the Successful Beginnings of the Lord Baltemore's Plantation in Maryland ; Being an extract of certain Letters written from thence, by some of the Adventurers to their friends in England. Anno Domini 1634. Square 8°, pp. 23.
  150 copies ; 34 large paper. Note by Brantz Mayer.

RULES and Regulations of the Maple-Grove Cemetery Association of the Town of Worcester, Otsego County, N. Y. 8°, pp. 32.
  500 copies.

ST. JOHN's College. Annual Catalogue. 8°, pp. 22.
  700 copies.

ST. STEPHEN's College. Annual Catalogue. 8°, pp. 18.
  400 copies.

SCHOHARIE County Bible Society. 8°, pp. 24.
  300 copies.

S. E. Further Queries upon the State of the New English Affairs. Square 8°, pp. iv, 18.
  250 copies ; 50 large paper.

SERMON. 8°, pp. 24.
  400 copies for Hotaling, printer at Johnstown.

SEVENTH Annual Catalogue of the Officers and Students of the Law School of Columbia College, for 1864–1865. 8°, pp. 40.

SEVENTH Annual Report of the Windham Association, Consociation and Benevolent Association, with Statistics of 1865 for the Churches. 8°, pp. 8.
  1,300 copies.

SEVENTEENTH Annual Report of the Albany Penitentiary. 8°, pp. 36.
  1,200 copies.

SHEPPARD, THOMAS. The Clear Sunshine of the Gospel Breaking Forth upon the Indians in New England. Square 8°, pp. xx, 56.
  250 copies ; 50 large paper.

STONE, WILLIAM L. Life of Joseph Brant (Thayendanegea) including the Border Wars of the American Revolution and Sketches of the Indian Campaigns of Generals Harmar, St. Clair, and Wayne, and other Matters connected with the Indian Relations of the United States and Great Britain, from the peace of 1783 to the Indian peace of 1795. 2 vols. 8°.
  500 copies ; 50 large paper. Portraits and plates.

STONE, WILLIAM L. The Life and Times of Sir William Johnson, Baronet. 2 vols. 8°.
  800 copies ; 50 large paper. Portraits and plates.

SUPPLEMENT to the State of the Expedition from Canada, containing Gen. Burgoyne's Orders, respecting the Principal Movements and Operations of the Army, to the raising of the Siege of Ticonderoga. 4to, pp. 26.
  75 copies. London, 1780, fac simile reprint.

TWENTY-NINTH Annual Report of the Albany City Tract and Missionary Society, presented at the Annual Meeting in the State Street Presbyterian Church, December 18, 1864. 8°, pp. 23.
1,000 copies.

TWOMBLY, A. S. Escape from Danger, a Cause for National Thanksgiving; a Discourse delivered in the State Street Presbyterian Church, on Thursday Morning, December 7, 1865. 4to, pp. 23.
225 copies.

WHITEHALL Transportation Company. 8°, pp. 26.
450 copies.

WHITFIELD, HENRY Strength out of Weakness; or a Glorious Manifestation of the Further Progress of the Gospel among the Indians in New England. Square 8°, pp. xvi, 59.
250 copies ; 50 large paper.

WOOD, B. The Dental Circular and Examiner. 8°, pp. 130.

1866.

ALBANY Zouave Cadets to the Rochester Union Blues. Square 8°, pp. 35.
250 copies.

ALLEN, L. An Essay on Motion and Force, read before the Albany Institute April 24, 1865. 8°, pp. 20.

ALLEN, R. L. Hand-Book of Saratoga, and Strangers' Guide. 12°, pp. 147.
500 copies.

ANDRÈ, JOHN. The Cow Chace, a Poem in three Cantos. By Major John Andrè, Adjutant General to the British Army in New York in 1780. Square 8°, pp. 69.
100 copies were printed for sale, and 30 copies for the editor Dr. F. B. Hough. Portrait and map. The work was withheld from the market.

ANNUAL Catalogue of the Officers and Students of Hartwick Theological and Classical Seminary, for the Academic year ending Aug. 23, 1866. 8°, pp. 12.
350 copies.

ANNUAL Report of the Methodist Sunday School Union. 8°, pp. 25.
600 copies.

ANNUAL Report of the Treasurer of Union College, made June 30, 1866. 8°, pp. 18.
50 copies.

ARTICLES of Association and Tariff of Rates for Fire Insurance, in the City of Albany, adopted by the Albany Board of Underwriters, 1866. 12°, pp. 69.
420 copies.

BENEDICT, HENRY M. A Memorial of Brevet Brigadier General Lewis Benedict, Colonel of 162d Regiment N. Y. V. I., who fell in the Battle at Pleasant Hill, La., April 9, 1864. Royal 8°, pp. 155.
200 copies privately printed. Portrait.

[BLOODGOOD, SIMEON DE WITT.] The Sexagenary, or Reminiscences of the American Revolution. 8°, pp. 234.
300 copies, and 50 large paper.

BOOKS, English and American, to be sold by Auction, Thursday and Friday, Dec. 13 and 14, by Bangs, Merwin & Co., at their Sales Rooms 694 and 696 Broadway, corner Fourth Street, New York. 8°, pp. 23.
500 copies. Books of W. Gowans.

BUDD, THOMAS. Good Order established in Pennsylvania and New Jersey in America, being a True Account of the Country; with its Produce and Commodities there made in the year 1685. By Thomas Budd. A New Edition, with an Introduction and copious Historical Notes, by Edward Armstrong. 8°, pp. 111.
500 copies, and 50 large paper.

BY-LAWS of Cambridge Valley Lodge. 16°, pp. 16.
500 copies.

BYRD, WILLIAM. History of the Dividing Line and other Tracts, from the Papers of William Byrd, of Westover, in Virginia, Esquire. 2 vols., square 8°. Vol. I. History of the Dividing Line. pp. xix, 233. Vol. II. Journey to the Land of Eden and other Tracts. pp. iv, 276.
200 copies, and 50 large paper.

CATALOGUE and Circular of the Albany Medical College. 8°, pp. 16.
600 copies.

CATALOGUE and Circular of the Young Ladies' Institute, No. 4 High Street, nearly opposite the Capitol, Albany, N. Y. Founded 1842. 8°, pp. 16.
200 copies.

CATALOGUE of a Choice Private Library, embracing a Rich Collection of Works on American History, Local History, Privately Printed Books including Munsell's and other Series, an Unique Collection of Books and Tracts relative to the City of New York, Books on the late War, and many very Rare Works on Irish History, etc. 8°, pp.36.
300 copies. Library of J. G. Shea, LL. D.

CATALOGUE of State Street Presbyterian Sunday School Library. 16°, pp. 40.
300 copies.

CATALOGUE of the Greenbush Methodist Episcopal Sunday School Library.
100 copies.

CATALOGUE of the Law School. 8°, pp. 8.
7,500 copies.

CATALOGUE of the Northfield Social Library, founded 1813. Small 8°, pp. 53.
75 copies. This was a donation, with 100 vols. of books, to the library where I obtained my first reading.

CATALOGUE of the Unitarian Sunday School Library.   16°, pp. 25.
　　100 copies.

CATALOGUE of the Valuable Library of FitzEdward Hall, Esq., D. C. L., to
　　be sold by Auction, Feb. 5, 1867, and following Days, by Leonard &
　　Co., at their Rooms, No. 50 Bromfield Street, Boston.   8°, pp. 354.
　　350 copies.

CAVERT, M. P.   The Study of the English Language and Literature as
　　an Educational Force; a Paper prepared by request, and read before
　　the New York State Teachers' Association at Geneva, in 1866.   8°,
　　pp. 12.

CHARLEVOIX, P. F. X. DE.   History and General Description of New
　　France, by the Rev. P. F. X. de Charlevoix, S. J., translated with
　　Notes, by John Gilmary Shea.   Vols. 1 and 2.   Sup. roy. 8°, pp. 286, 284.
　　Edition 250 copies.   Portraits, plates and maps.

CIRCULARS of Van Wormer and McGarvey's Stove Patterns.   8°, pp. 16.
　　1,000 copies.

CONSTITUTION and By-Laws of Schenevus Lodge of F.& A.M.   16°, pp. 16.
　　200 copies.

COVENANT and Membership of the State Street Presbyterian Church.   16°,
　　pp. 22.
　　100 copies.

CRUIKSHANK, JAMES.   The New York Teacher, a Monthly Journal of
　　School and Home Education.   Vol. XV.   pp. 386.
　　2,000 copies.

DICKSON.   Plans of the Capitol.   4°, pp. 39.
　　25 copies.

DREUILLETTES, GABRIELIS.   Epistola Rev. P. Gabrielis Dreuillettes, Soci-
　　tatis Jesu Presbyteri, ad Dominum Illustrissimum, Dominum Joannem
　　Winthrop, Scutarium.   8°, pp. 13.
　　110 copies.

DYER, DAVID.   Tests of Truth; Replies to Letters of a Skeptical Friend,
　　on the Teachings of Nature and Revealed Religion.   12°, pp. 209.
　　500 copies.

EIGHTEENTH Annual Report of the Inspectors of the Albany Penitentiary.
　　With the accompanying Documents.   Made 14th of December, 1865.
　　8°, pp. 36.
　　1,200 copies.

EIGHTH Annual Catalogue of the Officers and Students of the Law School,
　　Columbia College, for 1865–1866.   8°, pp. 40.
　　1,100 copies.

FIFTY-FIFTH Annual Report of the Albany County Bible Society, organized
　　A. D. 1810.   8°, pp. 16.
　　500 copies.

FORTY-EIGHTH Annual Report of the Bible Society of Fulton and Hamil-
　　ton Counties, presented at Johnstown, September 5, 1865, with Sta-
　　tistics.   8°, pp. 32.
　　500 copies.

GLAZIER, WILLARD W. The Capture, the Prison Pen and the Escape, giving an Account of Prison Life in the South, principally at Richmond, Danville, Macon, Savannah, Charleston, Columbia, Millin, Salisbury and Andersonville; describing the Arrival of Prisoners, Plans of Escape, with Incidents and Anecdotes of Prison Life: embracing, also the Adventures of an Escape from Columbia, S. C., Recapture, Trial as Spy, and Final Escape from Sylvania, Georgia. 12°, pp. 353.
450 copies.

GOWANS. Catalogue of Scarce American Books, for sale at the affixed Prices, Store 115 Nassau Street, New York. 8°, pp. 40.
1,750 copies.

HARSHA, DAVID A. Life of the Rev. George Whitefield. Royal 8°, pp. 66.

HARSHA, D. A. The Christian's Present for all Seasons; containing Devotional Thoughts of Eminent Divines, from Joseph Hall to William Jay. With an Introductory Essay on Devotion, by W. B. Sprague, D. D. Sup. roy. 8°, pp. xiv, 652.
Edition 18 copies from stereo. plates. Badly printed by a superannuated pressman.

HICKCOX, JOHN H. A History of the Bills of Credit or Paper Money issued by New York, from 1709 to 1789; with a Description of the Bills, and Catalogue of the Various Issues. Royal 8°, pp. 103.

HOUGH, FRANKLIN B. History of the Census in New York, and Plan proposed for he State Census of 1865; read before the Albany Institute, Dec. 19, 1864, and before the American Geographical and Statistical Society, Feb. 2, 1865. 8°, pp. 35.
50 copies.

HOUGH, FRANKLIN B. Notices of Peter Penet, and of his Operations among the Oneida Indians, including a Plan prepared by him for the Government of that Tribe. Read before the Albany Institute, January 23d, 1866. 8°, pp. 36.
50 copies.

HOUGH, FRANKLIN B. The Northern Invasion of October, 1780; a Series of Papers relating to the Expeditions from Canada under Sir John Johnson and others, against the Frontiers of New York, which were supposed to have connection with Arnold's Treason. Prepared from the original, with an Introduction and Notes, by Franklin B. Hough. 8°, pp. 224.
75 copies for sale; 80 for Club. 6th vol. Bradford Club Series. Plate of Brown's Monument.

JOURNAL of the Voyage of the Sloop Mary, from Quebeck, together with an Account of her Wreck off Montauk Point, L. I., Anno 1701. With Introduction and Notes by E. B. O'Callaghan. Square 8°, pp. 50.
100 copies; 25 for author.

KIP, REV. WILLIAM INGRAHAM. The Early Jesuit Missions in North America; compiled and translated from the Letters of the French Jesuits, with Notes. 12°, pp. xvi, 225.
1,000 copies. Map.

LAUS Patriæ Celestis. Translation of an Ancient Latin Hymn. By O. A. Morse. Small 8°, pp. 16.
100 copies. Privately printed.

LAW Cases and Points in the Supreme Court of the State of New York. 8°.
12 copies.

LAW Cases in the Court of Appeals of the State of New York.
20 copies.

LAW Points in the Supreme Court of the State of New York.
12 copies.

LAWS of the State of New York, passed at the Eighty-ninth Session of the Legislature, begun January second, and ended April twentieth, 1866, in the City of Albany. 2 vols., 8°, pp. 2150, 169.
3,500 copies.

LEONARD, HENRY C. Yea! and Nay! a Discourse on Christian Firmness and Courtesy, delivered in the First Unitarian Church, on Sunday Morning, April 22, 1866. 8°, pp. 21.

MANUAL of the Atlantic Mutual Life Insurance Company. 16°, pp. 88.
5,000 copies.

MASON'S Union. Laws. 8°, pp. 16.
100 copies.

MATHER, COTTON and ROBERT CALEF. The Witchcraft Delusion in New England; its Rise, Progress and Termination, as exhibited by Dr. Cotton Mather, in the Wonders of the Invisible World; and by Mr. Robert Calef, in his More Wonders of the Invisible World. With a Preface, Introduction and Notes, by Samuel G. Drake. 3 vols., square 8°, pp. cii, 247, xxix, 212, 244.
400 copies, and large paper 2 kinds.

MINUTES of the Particular Synod of Albany. 8°, pp. 41.
400 copies.

MINUTES of the Seventy-first Synod of the Evangelical Lutheran Ministerium of the State of New York and Adjacent Countries, held in St. Matthew's Church, New York, from Saturday, Oct. 13th, to Friday Oct. 19, 1866. 8°, pp. 69.
600 copies.

MINUTES of the Thirty-sixth Annual Convention of the Hartwick Synod of the Evangelical Lutheran Church in the State of New York, held at Brunswick, Rensselaer County, N. Y., Sept. 21–25, 1866. 8°, pp. 64.
1,000 copies.

MONROE and Gardiner's Imperishable Raw Hide Artificial Limbs, patented March 15, and Oct. 11, 1864, and July 25, 1865. 12°, pp. 19.

MORSE, F. W. Personal Experiences in the War of the Great Rebellion, from December, 1862, to July, 1865. 8°, pp. 152.
50 copies. Privately printed.

MUNSELL, JOEL. Webster's Calendar, or the Albany Almanac for the year of our Lord 1865. 12°, pp. 36.

NATIONAL Bureau of Education. Speech of James A. Garfield of Ohio in the House of Representatives, June 8, 1866, on a Bill to establish a National Bureau of Education. 8°, pp. 16.

PALMER, PETER S. History of Lake Champlain, from its first Exploration by the French in 1609, to the close of the year 1814. Royal 8°, pp. 276.
350 copies and 40 large paper. Diagrams of naval actions.

PALMER, RAY. The Highest Civilization a Result of Christianity and Christian Learning; a Discourse delivered at Norwich, Conn., Nov. 14, 1865, on behalf of the Society for Promoting Collegiate and Theological Education at the West, in Connection with the Annual Meeting of the Board of Directors. 8°, pp. 43.
1,000 copies.

PHELPS, E. J. A Sketch of the Life and Character of Charles Linsley, read before the Vermont Historical Society. 8°, pp. 20.
500 copies.

POUCHOT. Memoir upon the late War in North America, between the French and English, 1755–60; followed by Observations upon the Theatre of actual War, and by new Details concerning the Manners and Customs of the Indians; with Topographical Maps. Translated and edited by Franklin B. Hough, with additional Notes and Illustrations. 2 vols., sup. roy. 8°, pp. 268, 283.
150 copies, and 50 large paper.

PROCEEDINGS of the Fifty fourth Anniversary of the Washington County Bible Society, and other Anniversaries of Benevolent Associations, held at North White Creek, N. Y., Sept. 4th, 5th, and 6th, 1866. 12°, pp. 28.
500 copies.

PROCEEDINGS of the Fulton County Teachers' Institute, organized at the Public School House (District No. 21), at Gloversville, Fulton County, N. Y., beginning on Monday, October 20, and ending Oct. 13, 1865. 8°, pp. 20.
300 copies.

PUTLITZ. Forest Voices, Translated from the German of Putlitz; edited by Charles A. Smith. Small 8°, pp. 102.
500 copies, and 100 large paper.

READ, JOHN MEREDITH, JR. A Historical Inquiry concerning Henry Hudson, his Friends, Relatives and Early Life, his Connection with the Muscovy Company and Discovery of Delaware Bay. 8°, pp. 209.
700 copies, and 50 large paper. Hudson arms.

RECUEIL de Pièces sur Negociation entre la Nouvelle France et la Nouvelle Angleterre, des années 1648 et suivantes. Small 8°, pp. 63.
160 copies.

SEMI-CENTENNIAL Anniversary of the Second R. P. Dutch Church Sabbath School, Albany, N. Y., Sunday evening, April 1, 1866. 12°, pp. 8.

SERMON before the Unitarian Society. 8°, pp. 20.
300 copies.

SIEGE of Savannah, by the combined American and French Forces, under the command of Gen. Lincoln and the Count D'Estaing, in the Autumn of 1779. Cap 4°, pp. 187.
100 copies, for sale and 30 for editor. Portrait Maj. Gen. Thomas Pinckney. Edited by Dr. F. B. Hough.

SIMS, CLIFFORD STANLEY. The Institution of the Society of the Cincinnati, together with the Roll of the Original, Hereditary, and Honorary Members of the Order, in the State of New Jersey, from 1783 to 1866. 8°, pp. 79.
100 copies. Considerable alterations were directed to be made after the whole was printed, and the editor's name stricken from the title page.

SKETCH. C. B. Gilmary. 8°, pp. 25.
200 copies.

[SPENCER, SPENCE.] The Scenery of Ithaca, and the Head Waters of the Cayuga Lake, as portrayed by different Writers, and edited by the Publisher. 16°, pp. 152.
1,200 copies.

STONE, WILLIAM L. The Life and Times of Sa-go-ye-wat-ha, or Red Jacket, with a Memoir of the Author, by his Son. 8°, pp. 510.
500 copies, and 50 large paper, and 25 4to. Portrait W. L. Stone, and of Red Jacket, and plate of Red Jacket medal and his residence.

STREET, ALFRED B. Frontenac, a Poem of the Iroquois. 4°, pp. xiv, 324.
300 copies.

TESTELIN and WARLOMONT. Glaucoma and its Cure by Iridectomy; translated by C. A. Robertson, from the French. 8°, pp. 40.
500 copies.

THIRTIETH Annual Report of the Albany City Tract and Missionary Society, presented at the Annual Meeting in the North Dutch Church, December 24, 1865. 8°, pp. 25.
1,000 copies.

THIRTY-FIFTH Anniversary of the Stephentown Baptist Association, held in the Baptist Church in Petersburgh, Sept. 12 and 13, 1866. 8°, pp. 16.
400 copies.

To the Legislature of the State of New York. 8°, pp. 10.

TOWNSEND, HOWARD. Food and its Digestion; read before the Albany Institute, Feb. 27, 1865. 8°, pp. 18.
250 copies.

TOWNSEND, HOWARD. The Sinai Bible, or Bibliorum Codex Sinaiticus Petropolitanus; read before the Albany Institute, Dec. 15, 1863. 8°, pp. 14.
150 copies.

TYLER, R. H. American Ecclesiastical Law ; the Law of Religious Societies, Church Government and Creeds, disturbing Religious Meetings, and the Law of Burial Grounds in the United States, with Practical Forms. 8°, pp. viii, 538.

WORTH, GORHAM A. Random Recollections of Albany, from 1800 to 1808 ; third Edition, with Notes by the Publisher. 8°, pp. 134.
400 copies, and 50 large paper.

1867.

ALEXANDER, O. C. Ino of the Glen. A Poem. 8°, pp. 22.

ALLAN, GEORGE H. Memoir of Col. John Allan, an Officer of the Revolution, born in Edinburgh Castle, Scotland, Jan. 3, 1746 ; died in Lubec, Maine, Feb. 7, 1805 ; with a Genealogy. 8°, pp. 32.

ARCHÆOLOGICAL Curiosities of the Rituals of Freemasonry, as displayed in the so-called Exposures of Freemasonry that have appeared since the Revival of Masonry in 1817 : consisting of a faithful Reprint of some of the Rarest and most curious of those Pamphlets. No. I. The Grand Mystery Discovered. Cap 4°, pp. 12.

ARCHÆOLOGICAL Curiosities, etc. No. II. Masonry dissected. Cap 4°, pp. 22.

BERGEN, TEUNIS G. Genealogy of the Van Brunt Family, 1653–1867. 8°, pp. 79.

CATALOGUE of a Collection of Books, chiefly Works relating to the History of America, general and local, including many Scarce and Valuable Books on the Western Country, Indian Narratives, etc., a small Collection of Voyages and Travels, also scarce Bibliographical Books, etc., being a portion of the Private Library of a Western Gentleman, to be sold by Auction, on Tuesday, Dec. 10, 1867, and following Days, by Bangs, Merwin & Co. 8°, pp. 138.

CATALOGUE of a Collection of Miscellaneous Books, including American Historical Works, English Books, and Classics, in fine Editions, to be sold at Auction on Monday afternoon, May 20, 1867, by Bangs, Merwin & Co., at their Sales Rooms, 694 and 696 Broadway, New York. 8°, pp. 16.

CATALOGUE of Books. 8°, pp. 32.

CATALOGUE of the Valuable Library of FitzEdward Hall, Esq., D.C.L., to be sold at Auction on Tuesday, Feb. 5, 1867, and following Days, by Leonard & Co., at their Rooms No. 50 Bromfield Street, Boston. 8°, pp. 352.
750 copies.

CASES in the Court of Appeals of the State of New York. 8°.
25 copies.

CASES in the Supreme Court of the State of New York.   Sup. roy. 8°.
25 copies.

CONSTITUTION and By-Laws and Tariff of Rates for Fire Insurance in
Hudson, N. Y., adopted by the Hudson Board of Underwriters.   12°,
pp. 48.
100 copies.

CONSTITUTION of the Albany Coachman's Benevolent Union, organized
May 18, 1867.   16°, pp. 16.

CONSTITUTION of the Bible and Prayer Book Society, of Albany and its
Vicinity, incorporated A.D. 1820.   12°, pp. 11.

CRUIKSHANK, JAMES.   The New York Teacher, a Monthly Journal of
School and Home Education.   Vol. XVI.   8°, pp. 368.

DANKERS and SLUYTER.   Journal of a Voyage to New York, and a Tour
in several of the American Colonies in 1679–80, by Jasper Dankers
and Peter Sluyter, of Wiewerd, in Friesland.   Translated from the
Original manuscript in Dutch for the Long Island Historical Society,
by Hon. Henry C. Murphy.   8°, pp. viii, xlvii, 440.
1,000 copies and 100 large paper.   Views, etc.

DESCRIPTIVE Catalogue of the Bunyan Tableaux.   12°, pp. 38.

DOTY, LOCKWOOD L.   History of Livingston County, New York.   8°, pp. 3.

DRAKE, SAMUEL G.   The Old Indian Chronicle; being a Collection of
exceeding Rare Tracts, written and published in the Time of King
Philip's War, by Persons residing in the Country; to which are now
added an Introduction and Notes.   Square 8°, pp. xi, 333.

DUER, WILLIAM A.   Reminiscences of an Old Yorker.   Imp. 8°, pp. 102.
35 copies.

DYER, DAVID.   History of the Penitentiary.   8°, pp. 273.

EARLE, JOHN.   Microcosmography, or a Piece of the World Discovered,
in Essays and Characters; to which are added Notes and an Appendix,
by Philip Bliss.   First American Edition, edited by L. L. Williams
[William L. Learned.]   Small 8°, pp. xvi, 277.

FIFTEENTH Annual Report of the Commissioners of the Alms-House of
the City and Town of Newburgh.   8°, pp. 25.
Engraving of Alms House.

FIFTY-SIXTH Annual Report of the Albany County Bible Society, organized A. D. 1810.   8°, pp. 19.

GOWANS.   Catalogue of Theological Books, for sale at the affixed Prices.
Discount to the Trade.   Store 115 Nassau Street, New York.   8°,
pp. 52.

HAVERTY, P. M.   Catalogue of a Valuable and Rare Collection of Roman Catholic Theology, comprising Works on Biblical Hermeneutics, Moral and Dogmatic Theology, Philosophy, Canon Law, Liturgy, Ritual, Councils, Ascetism, Church Music, Archæology, Rules and Constitutions, Biography, Bibliography, Sermons, &c., in Latin, French, and Italian.   8°, pp. 24.

HOUGH, FRANKLIN B.   Proceedings of a Convention of Delegates from several of the New England States, held at Boston, Aug. 3–9, 1780; to advise on Affairs necessary to promote the most vigorous Prosecution of the War, and to provide for a generous Reception of our French Allies.   Edited from an original Manuscript Record in the New York State Library, with an Introduction and Notes.   Square 8°, pp. 80.
   Map.

HOWARD, NATHAN, JR.   Practice Reports in the Supreme Court and Court of Appeals of the State of New York.   Vol. XXVII.   8°, pp. 602.

HOWARD, NATHAN, JR.   Practice Reports in the Supreme Court and Court of Appeals of the State of New York.   Vol. XXXI.   8°, pp. iv, 641.

IN Memoriam.   David L. Seymour.   Born December 2, 1803.   Died October 11, 1867.   Sup. roy. 8°, pp. 60.

IN Memoriam.   Howard Townsend, M.D., died January 16, 1867.   Small 8°. pp. 41.

JANES, FREDERICK.   The Janes Family, a Genealogy and Brief History of the Descendants of William Janes, the Emigrant Ancestor of 1637, with an extended Notice of Bishop Edmund S. Janes, D.D., and other Biographical Sketches.   8°, pp. 419.
   380 copies.   4 photograph portraits.

JONES, CHARLES C., JR.   Historical Sketch of the Chatham Artillery during the Confederate Struggle for Independence.   Royal 8°, pp. 240.
   Three plans.

KIDDER, FREDERIC.   Military Operations in Eastern Maine and Nova Scotia during the Revolution, chiefly compiled from the Journals and Letters of Col. John Allan, with Notes and a Memoir of Col. John Allan.   8°, pp. x, 336.
   Map.

LAURENS, COL. JOHN.   The Army Correspondence of Col. John Laurens in the year 1777–78, now first Printed from Original Letters addressed to his Father, Henry Laurens, President of Congress, with a Memoir by Wm. Gilmore Simms.   8°, pp. 250.

LAW Points in the Supreme Court.   Sup. roy. 8°.

LINTNER, G. A.   The Early History of the Lutheran Church in the State of New York, a discourse delivered before the Hartwick Synod in the Lutheran Church of Richmondville, N. Y., Sept. 21, 1867.   8°, pp. 24.

MANUAL of the Board of Instruction of the City of Albany. 8°, pp. 40.

MAYER, BRANTZ. Tah-gah-jute, or Logan and Cresap, an Historical Essay. 8°, pp. x, 204.

MEMORIAL Volume of the Semi-Centennial Anniversary of Hartwick Seminary, held Aug. 21, 1866. 8°, pp. 201.

MEMORIALS of Clark B. Cochrane. 8°, pp. 114.
Portrait.

MINUTES of the Seventy-first Anniversary of the Rensselaerville Association, held with the Baptist Church of Rensselaerville, Albany County, N. Y., Sept. 4 and 5, 1867. 8°, pp. 15.

MINUTES of the Thirty-seventh Annual Convention of the Hartwick Synod of the Evangelical Lutheran Church in the State of New York, held at Richmondville, Schoharie County, N. Y., Sept. 20–25, 1867. 8°, pp. 52.

MORSE, O. A. A Vindication of the Claim of Alexander M. W. Ball, of Elizabeth, N. J. to the Authorship of the Poem, Rock me to Sleep Mother: with an Introductory Note from Luther R. Marsh. 8°, pp. 70.
3,000 copies.

MOSES, HALSEY H. The Law of Mandamus and the Practice connected with it, with an Appendix of Forms. 8°, pp. 268.

MOSHER, JACOB S. Water and its Impurities, with Reference to the Supply of Large Towns, read before the Albany Institute, March 20, 1866. 8°, pp. 22.

MUNSELL, J. Collections on the History of Albany, from its Discovery to the Present Time, with Notices of its Public Institutions, and Biographical Sketches of Citizens deceased. Vol. II. Sup. roy. 8°, pp. 507.
Portraits and Plates.

MUNSELL, JOEL. Webster's Calendar, or the Albany Almanac for the year of our Lord 1868. 12°, pp. 36.

NATIONAL Educational Associations, 1866. Proceedings and Lectures of the National Teachers' Association, the National Association of School Superintendents, and the American Normal School Association, at their Annual Meetings, held in Indianapolis, Ind., Aug., 1866. 8°, pp. 139.

O'CALLAGHAN, E. B. Voyage of George Clarke, Esq., to America; with Introduction and Notes. Cap 4°, pp. lxxxi, 126.
Photograph of Clarke Monument.

O'CALLAGHAN, E. B. Voyages of the Slavers St. John and Arms of Amsterdam 1659, 1663: together with Additional Papers illustrative of the Slave Trade under the Dutch. Translated from the Original Manuscripts, with an Introduction and Index. Cap. 4°, pp. xxxii, 255.

PARTING Words from Rev. Alex. S. Twombly, to his Friends and Parishioners, Jan. 20, 1867, State Street Presbyterian Church, Albany, N. Y. 8°, pp. 20.

PRINCIPLES and Practice of Life Insurance as maintained by the Atlantic Mutual Life Insurance Company of Albany, N. Y. 16°, pp. 52.

PROCEEDINGS of the Board of Supervisors of the County of Saratoga, for 1866. 8°, pp. 204.

PROCEEDINGS of the Convention and Minutes of the First Session of the Evangelical Lutheran Synod of the State of New York, held in St. Paul's Church, Red Hook, from Friday, Oct. 18, to Tuesday, Oct. 22, 1867. 8°, pp. 23.

RECORD of the Class of 1854. Yale. Personal Statistics of Thirteen years. Published by order of the Class. 8°, pp. 100.

RIEDESEL. Letters and Journals relating to the War of the American Revolution and the Capture of the German Troops at Saratoga, by Mrs. General Riedesel; translated from the Original German, by William L. Stone. pp. 235.
200 copies, and 50 large paper, 25 quarto, portrait of Madame Riedesel and engravings on wood.

ROCHESTER Almanac, for the year of our Lord 1867, with a Business Mirror, representing Enterprising and Reliable Firms of the City. 12°, pp. 36.
5,000 copies.

RULES of the Board of Supervisors of the County of Saratoga, in relation to auditing Accounts of Justices of the Peace, Police Justices, Deputy Sheriffs, Constables, Coroners and Printers, with the Tariff of Fees, fixed by Law for their Services. 8°, pp. 16.

SABIN, JOSEPH. Catalogue of a small but select Collection of Books, from a Private Library, for sale at the very low Prices affixed. 8°, pp. 40.

SIEGE of Charleston, by the British Fleet and Army under the Command of Admiral Arbuthnot and Sir Henry Clinton, which terminated with the Surrender of that Place, on the 12th of May, 1780. Cap. 4°, pp. 224.
100 copies for sale, and 30 for editor. Portraits of Maj. Gen. Benjamin Lincoln and David Ramsay. Edited by Dr. F. B. Hough.

SMITH, E. PESHINE. Reports of Cases argued and determined in the Court of Appeals of the State of New York. Vol. X. 8°, pp. 688.

SMITH, E. PESHINE. Reports of Cases argued and determined in the Court of Appeals of the State of New York. Vol. XII. 8°, pp. 688.

STILES, HENRY R. A History of the City of Brooklyn, including the Old Town and Villages of Brooklyn, the Town of Bushwick, and the Village and City of Williamsburgh. Vol. I. 8°, pp. viii, 464.
1,000 copies, 80 large paper, 100 fine paper. Plates and maps.

TARIFF of Rates for Fire Insurance, adopted by the Board of Underwriters, Plattsburgh, N. Y. 12°. pp. 32.
100 copies.

TARIFF of Rates for Fire Insurance in the Village of Amsterdam, and Vicinity. 12°, pp. 14.
100 copies.

THIRTY-FIRST Annual Report of the Albany City Tract and Missionary Society, presented at the Annual Meeting in the Fourth Presbyterian Church, December 23, 1866.   8°, pp. 24.
1,000 copies.

THOMPSON, ISAAC GRANT.   The Law and Practice of Provisional Remedies, with an Appendix of Forms.   8°, pp. 712.

TRANSACTIONS of the Albany Institute.   Vol. V.   pp. viii, 337.
Plates.

VINCENT, MARVIN R.   Amusement, a Force in Christian Training.   Four Discourses.   12°, pp. 140.
1,000 copies.

WORTH, GORHAM A.   Random Recollections of Albany, from 1800 to 1808 ; third edition, with Notes by the Publisher.   Sup. roy. 8°, pp. 144.
50 large paper ; 300 small.

1868.

AMERICAN Railway Literary Union : Synopsis of Principles and Plan. 8°, pp. 4.

ANTHONY, JOSEPH.   Forms of Rail Road Car Axles.   8°, pp. 15.
Illustrations.

BERKSHIRE County Almanac for the year of our Lord 1868.   12°, pp. 36.

[BOGART, WM. H., and DAUGHTERS.]   Quentin Durward, the Loser and the Winner.   Privately Printed.   16°, pp. 69.

BOTT, ARTHUR.   Prussia and the German System of Education.   Read before the Albany Institute, February, 1867.   8°, pp. 66.

BROWNE, IRVING.   A Parlor Comedy.   Our Best Society ; being an Adaptation of the Potiphar Papers, in four Acts.   8°, pp. 50.
Tinted paper, old style type.

CAMPBELL, CHARLES.   Genealogy of the Spotswood Family in Scotland and Virginia.   8°, pp. 44.

CAMPBELL, CHARLES.   Some Materials to serve for a Brief Memoir of John Daly Burk, author of a History of Virginia, with a Sketch of the Life and Character of his only Child, Judge John Junius Burk.   8°, pp. 122

CATALOGUE of Books on Printing and the Kindred Arts : embracing also Works on Copyright, Liberty of the Press, Libel, Literary Property, Bibliography, etc.   8°, iv, 47.

CATALOGUE of the Library of the State Street Presbyterian Church Sabbath School, Albany.   16°, pp. 43.

CHARLEVOIX, P. F. X. DE. History and General Description of New France, by the Rev. P. F. X. de Charlevoix, S. J., translated with Notes, by John Gilmary Shea. Vol. III. Sup. roy. 8°.
Edition, 250 copies. Portraits, plates and maps.

DEAN, AMOS. The History of Civilization. Vol. I. 8°, pp. xxiv, 695.
Edition, 800 copies, portrait.

DEAN, JOHN WARD. A Memoir of Rev. Nathaniel Ward, A. M., author of the Simple Cobler of Agawam in America, with Notices of his Family. 8°, pp. 213.

DE COSTA, B. F. The Pre-Columbian Discovery of America by the Northmen, illustrated by Translations from the Icelandic Sagas, edited with Notes and a General Introduction. 8°, pp. lx, 118.
Map of Cape Cod.

DEDICATION Services of the Lowville Rural Cemetery, October 9, 1867; together with the Articles and By-Laws of the Association. 8°, pp. 24.

DURRIE, DANIEL S. Bibliographia Genealogica Americana; an Alphabetical Index to American Genealogies and Pedigrees contained in State, County and Town Histories, Printed Genealogies, and Kindred Works. 8°, pp. xii, 296.

FIFTY-SEVENTH Annual Report of the Albany County Bible Society organized A.D. 1810. 8°, pp. 16.

FISHER, E. T. Report of a French Protestant Refugee, in Boston, 1687; translated from the French. Cap 4°, pp. 42.

GILMAN, ARTHUR. The Gilman Family traced in the line of Hon. John Gilman of Exeter, N. H.. with an Account of many other Gilmans in England and America. Cap 4°, pp. xiv, 324.
$5. ed. 250 cop. $20. ed. 20 cop.

GOWANS. Catalogue of Miscellaneous Books, for sale at the affixed Prices, Discount to the Trade. Store 115 Nassau street, New York. 8°, pp. 40.

HALL, HILAND. The History of Vermont, from its Discovery to its Admission into the Union in 1791. 8°, pp. xii, 521.
Map.

HALL, PROF. JAMES. Report on Building Stones. 8°, pp. 67.

HINTS on Writing. 8°, pp. 14.

[HUN, THOMAS.] Proposed By-Laws of the Medical Society of the State of New York. 8°, pp. 17.

JONES, CHARLES C., Jr. Historical Sketch of Tomo-chi-chi, Mico of the Yamacraws. 8°, pp. viii, 133.

KIDDER, FREDERIC. History of the First New Hampshire Regiment in the War of the Revolution. 8°, pp. viii, 184.

LAWS relating to the New Capitol at Albany. 8°, pp. 8.

MACY, SYLVANUS J. Genealogy of the Macy Family from 1635–1868. 4°, pp. 457.
>Portraits and fac-simile documents.

MEMOIRS, and Letters and Journals, of Major General Riedesel, during his Residence in America. Translated from the Original German of Max Von Eelking, by William L. Stone. 2 vols., 8°.
>Portrait of General Riedesel, plates of house in which Col. Baum died, and of the Smith house.

MINUTES of the Seventy-second Anniversary of the Rensselaerville Association, held with the Baptist Church at Sloansville, Schoharie County, N. Y., Sept. 2, 3, and 4, 1868. 8°, pp. 16.

MORRELL, T. H. Catalogue of a Valuable Collection of Rare and Standard English Books, Ancient and Modern ; comprising many Unique and beautiful Volumes; Works on America, Shakespeare, the Drama, Poetry, History, Biography, etc., together with a few engravings, for sale at the low prices affixed. 8°, pp. 28.

MORRELL, T. H. Catalogue of Books (lacks title) 8°, pp. 42.

MOSES, HALSEY H. The Law of Mandamus, and the Practice connected with it, with an Appendix of Forms. 8°, pp. iv, 268.

MUNSELL, CHARLES. A Collection of Songs of the American Press, and other Poems relating to the art of Printing. Small 8°, pp. viii, 207.

MUNSELL, JOEL. Webster's Calendar, or the Albany Almanac for the year of our Lord 1869. 12°, pp. 36.

NEILL, EDWARD D. The Fairfaxes of England and America in the Seventeenth and Eighteenth Centuries, including Letters from and to Hon. William Fairfax, President of Council of Virginia, and his sons, Col. George William Fairfax, and Rev. Bryan, Eighth Lord Fairfax, the Neighbors and Friends of George Washington. 8°, pp. 234.

NORTH, EDWARD. Memorial of Henry Hastings Curran, Lieutenant Colonel of the One Hundred and Forty-Sixth Regiment of the New York State Volunteers. Privately printed. 8°, pp. 223.
>Should have a portrait.

OLMSTEAD, Vaux & Co. Report on the Proposed City Park. 8°, pp. 14.

OUR Financial Credit abroad: Commissioner Wells on the United States National Debt. 8°, pp. 8.

[PEARSON, JONATHAN.] A General Catalogue of the Officers, Graduates and Students of Union College, from 1795 to 1868. 8°, pp. 155.

PEARSON, JONATHAN. Early Records of the City and County of Albany, and Colony of Rensselaerswyck (1656–1675). Translated from the Original Dutch, with Notes. Sup. roy. 8°, pp. vii, 528.

PORTER, CHARLES H., M. D. Paper on Building Stones. To the New Capitol Commissioners. 8°, pp. 41.

PROCEEDINGS of the Fifty-Fifth Anniversary of the Washington County Bible Society, and other Anniversaries of Benevolent Associations, held at South Argyle, N. Y., Sept. 3d, 4th and 5th, 1867. 12°, pp. 35.

SABIN, JOSEPH. Catalogue of Books in various Departments of Literature, for sale at the Moderate Prices affixed, by Joseph Sabin, 84 Nassau street, New York, being a Selection from a Stock of about 40,000 volumes constantly on sale. 8°, pp. 32.

SABIN, JOSEPH. Catalogue of the Library collected by the late Professor Amos Dean, of Albany, N. Y., principally with reference to his History of Man as unfolded in his Civilization ; now offered for sale at the very moderate Prices affixed. 8°, pp. 186.

SABIN, J. & Sons. Recent Publications of J. Munsell, for sale by J. Sabin & Sons, 84 Nassau Street, New York; Books of small Editions sold at the net Prices affixed. 8°, pp. 8.

SECOND Annual Report of the Atlantic Mutual Life Insurance Company. 16°, pp. 36.
  10,000 copies.

SHEPARD, A. K. Papers on Spanish America. 8vo, pp. 75.
  Tinted paper.

SMITH, CHARLES ADAM. Before the Flood and after. 8°, pp. 228.

STUDY of Words. 8°, pp. 22.

TENNEY, JONATHAN. Memorial of the Class graduated at Dartmouth College, July 27, 1843 ; with Notices of its Septenary Meetings ; also Sketches and Tables, Biographical and Statistical, for the first Twenty-five Years of the Class History, of all who were ever Members of the Class. Prepared at the Request and for the Use of the Class. 8°, pp. 164.

THE Pattern Man. A Comedy in five Acts. Not published, but confidentially communicated by the Author. 12°, pp. 107.

THIRTY-SECOND Annual Report of the Albany City Tract and Missionary Society, presented at the Annual Meeting in the Second Presbyterian Church, December 22, 1867. 8°, pp. 24.
  1,000 copies.

WHITMORE, WILLIAM H. The American Genealogist, being a Catalogue of Family Histories and Publications containing Genealogical Information issued in the United States, arranged Chronologically. 8°, pp. 287.

WHITNEY, H. R. Heart Lyrics. 12°, pp. 114.
  The author died while the work was in press.

WILLIAMS, C. P. A Review of the Financial Situation of Our Country. 8°, pp. 46.

WILSON, REV. F. F. Memorial Volume of the Semi-Centennial Anniversary of the Second Reformed Church of Glenville, N. Y., Nov. 21, 1868. 8°, pp. 61.

1869.

ADDRESS delivered on Tuesday Evening, June 15, 1869, at the Close of the Anniversary Exercises of the Young Ladies Institute, Albany, by William B. Sprague, D.D. 8°, pp. 12.

ALSOP, GEORGE. A Character of the Province of Maryland, wherein is described in Four distinct Parts (Viz.) 1. The Scituation, and Plenty of the Province. II. The Laws, Customs and natural Demeanor of the Inhabitants. III. The worst and best Vsage of a Maryland Servant, opened in view. IV. The Traffique, and Vendable Commodities of the Countrey. Also, a Small Treatise on the Wilde and Naked Indians (or Susquehanokes), of Maryland, their Customs, Manners, Absurdities and Religion. Together with a Collection of Historical Letters. London. Printed by T. J., for Peter Dring, at the Sign of the Sun in the Poultrey, 1666. A new Edition, with an Introduction and Copious Historical Notes, by John Gilmary Shea. 8°, pp. 125.

ANNUAL Catalogue of the Officers and Students of the Hartwick Theological and Classical Seminary, for the Academic year ending June 30, 1869. 8°, pp. 12.

ANNUAL Report of the Water Commissioners of the City of Newburgh, for the year ending March 9, 1869. 8°, pp. 35.

BROCKWAY, J., SEN. An Introductory Lecture delivered before the Third District Dental Association of the State of New York, at their first Meeting after Organization, Jan. 12, 1869. Synopsis of Dentistry, as it was, as it is, and as it ought to be, a Power to move and mend the World. 8°, pp. 23.

BY-LAWS of Ancient City Lodge No. 452, F. and A. M., of the City of Albany and State of New York. Chartered Oct. 15, A. L. 5858 : Incorporated June 15, A. L. 5868. 16°, pp. 88.

CATALOGUE of Books in the Library of the First Congregational Sabbath School, June, 1869. 16°, pp. 30.

CATALOGUE of Library of St. Paul's Evangelical Lutheran Sabbath School, Red Hook, N. Y. 16°, pp. 23.

CATALOGUE of Rare, Useful and Curious Books, Tracts, &c., in American Literature; chiefly Historical and Descriptive of the United States : Selected as important in every Private and Public Library pretending at all to a Department of American History, on sale at the prices annexed, at his Office, No. 17 Bromfield Street (up stairs), by Samuel G. Drake. 8°, pp. 70.

CATALOGUE of the Officers and Students of the Law School connected with the University of Albany for the Academical year 1869–70. 8°, pp. 16.

CATALOGUE of the Officers and Students of the New York State Normal School, for the Fiftieth Term, ending July 1, 1869. 8°, pp. 16.

CIRCULAR and Catalogue of the Law School connected with the University of Albany, for the year 1869–70. 8°, pp. 12.

DEAN, AMOS. The History of Civilization. Vols. II to VII, 8°.
800 copies.

DECOSTA, B. F. Sailing Directions of Henry Hudson, prepared for his use in 1608, from the old Danish of Ivar Bardsen ; with an Introduction and Notes ; also a Dissertation on the Discovery of the Hudson River. 8,° pp. 102.

DRAKE, SAMUEL G. Annals of Witchcraft in New England, and Elsewhere in the United States, from their first Settlement. Drawn up from unpublished and other well authenticated Records of the alleged operations of Witches and their Instigator, the Devil. Cap 4°, pp. 306.
Portrait of John Wentworth.

DREUILLETTES, GABRIELIS. Epistola Rev. P. Gabrielis Dreuillettes Societatis Jesu Presbyteri, ad Dominum Illustrissimum, Dominum Joannem Wintrop, Scutarium. 8°, pp. 14.

FIFTY-EIGHTH Annual Report of the Albany County Bible Society, organized A. D. 1810. 8°, pp. 16.

FRANCIS, DAVID G. A Catalogue of Sterling New and old Books, including many Scarce Books in American History, Old English Literature, Voyages and Travels, Poetry and the Drama, Facetiæ, &c., &c., many of which are in fine Bindings, for sale at the reasonable prices affixed. 8°, pp. 28.

F ROTHINGHAM, WASHINGTON. Martel Papers ; or Life Scenes in the Reign of Terror [circular respecting]. 8°, pp. 8.

GOWANS. Catalogue of American Books, for sale at the affixed Prices. Store 115 Nassau street, New York. 8°, pp. 28.

HAMILTON College. Curran Prize Examination, March 27, 1869. 8°, pp. 8.

HAVERTY, P. M. Part 2. Catalogue of a Valuable and Rare Collection of Roman Catholic Theology, comprising Works on Biblical Hermeneutics, Moral and Dogmatic Theology, Philosophy, Canon Law, Liturgy, Rubrics, Ritual, Councils, Ascetism, Archæology, Rules and Constitutions, Biography, Bibliography, Sermons, etc., in Latin and French ; for sale at No. 1 Barclay St., N. Y. 8°, pp. 24.

HOUGH, G. W. Remarks on the Galvanic Battery. 8°, pp. 13.

HOUGH, G. W. Velocity of the Electric Current over Telegraph Wire, read before the Albany Institute, June, 1869. 8°, pp. 12.

HOWARD, NATHAN, JR. Practice Reports in the Supreme Court and Court of Appeals of the State of New York. 8°. Vol. XXV   pp. iv, 594.

HOWARD, NATHAN, JR.   Practice Reports in the Supreme Court and Court of Appeals of the State of New York.   8°,   Vol. XXXIII, pp. iv, 620.

HUN, EDWARD R.   The Trichina Spiralis.   8°, pp. 10.

LANSING, JOHN V.   Frogs and their Contributions to Science.   8°, pp. 18.

LAST Illness of Dr. Alden March.   8°, pp. 11.

LAW Cases in the Supreme Court of the State of New York.   Sup. roy. 8°.

LAW Points in the Court of Appeals of the State of New York.   2 vols., sup. roy. 8°.

LAW Points in the Supreme Court of the State of New York. 2 vols., sup. roy. 8°.

MINUTES of the Third Annual Session of the Evangelical Lutheran Synod of the State of New York, held in St. Matthew's Church, Brooklyn, N. Y., from Thursday, Oct. 21, to Tuesday, Oct. 26, 1869.   8°, pp. 35.

MUNSELL, JOEL.   Annals of Albany. vol. I, 2d edition.   12°, pp. viii, 434.
   Plates.

MUNSELL, JOEL.   Webster's Calendar, or the Albany Almanac for the year of our Lord 1870.   12°, pp. 36.

NASON, ELIAS.   A Monogram on our National Song.   8°, pp. 69.

NEILL, EDWARD D.   Pocahontas and her Companions ; a Chapter from the History of the Virginia Company of London.   Square 8°, pp. 32.
   Portrait.

NINTH CENSUS.   Letter and Extracts from Testimonials accompanying the Application of Dr. Franklin B. Hough, for appointment as Superintendent of the Ninth Census.   8°, pp. 13.

PARKER, AMASA J.   Reports of Decisions in Criminal Cases made at Term in Chambers and in the Courts of Oyer and Terminer of the State of New York.   Vol. VI.   8°, pp. 727.

PROCEEDINGS of the Sixty-Sixth Anniversary of the Washington County Bible Society, and other Anniversaries of Benevolent Associations, held at Salem, N. Y., Sept. 2d and 3d, 1868.   12°, pp. 20.

SECOND Annual Report of the Albany City Dispensary Association, presented October 5, 1869 ; No. 7 Plain Street.   8°, pp. 12.

SEVENTH Annual Catalogue of St. Stephen's College, Annandale, N. Y., 1868–69.   8°, pp. 29.

SMITH, E. PESHINE.   Reports of Cases argued and determined in the Court of Appeals of the State of New York.   Vol. IX.   8°, pp. 667.

SMITH, E. PESHINE.   Reports of Cases argued and determined in the Court of Appeals of the State of New York.   Vol. XII.   8°, pp. 652.

SMITH, WILLIAM R.   Diomede: from the Iliad of Homer.   8°, pp. 52.

STEVENS, GEORGE T.   Life as a Physical Phenomenon ; read before the Albany Institute, May 5, 1869.   8°, pp. 22.

STILES, HENRY R.   A History of the City of Brooklyn, including the old Town and Village of Brooklyn, the Town of Bushwick, and the Village and City of Williamsburgh.   Vol. II.   Sup. roy. 8°, pp. 500.
Plates, maps and plates.

STILES, HENRY REED.   Bundling ; its Origin, Progress and Decline in America.   16°, pp. 139.
Old style type.

THIRTY-THIRD Annual Report of the Albany City Tract and Missionary Society, presented at the Annual Meeting, in the First Reformed church, December 21, 1868.   8°, pp. 24.
1,000 copies.

THOMAS, ELIJAH L.   An Abridged Genealogy of the Olmstead Family of New England.   16°, pp. 30.

TIFFANY, JOEL.   Reports of Cases in the Court of Appeals of the State of New York, with Notes, References, and an Index.   Vol. XII.   8°, pp. 547.

TWENTY-FIRST Annual Report of the Inspectors of the Albany Penitentiary, with the accompanying Documents.   Made December 16, 1869.   8°, pp. 47.

WARD, DURBIN.   Shaker Income Tax : Application to Commissioner Delano.   8°, pp. 21.

WATSON, WINSLOW C.   The Military and Civil History of the County of Essex, New York ; and a General Survey of its Physical Geography, its Mines and Minerals, and Industrial Pursuits : embracing an Account of the Northern Wilderness ; and also the Military Annals of the Fortresses of Crown Point and Ticonderoga.   8°, pp. viii, 504.
Portraits and plates.

YATES, PETER W.   An Address delivered in the Lodge Room at Schenectady the 27th of December, 1783, on the Festival of St. John the Evangelist, in Presence of the Officers and Brethren of Union Lodge, No. 1 of the City of Albany, St. George's Lodge of Schenectady, and several visiting Brethren of the Most Ancient and Honorable Society of Free and Accepted Masons.   By Peter W. Yates, Counsellor at Law, and Master of said Union Lodge.   Albany, printed by S. Ballentine, 1784.   Cap 8°, pp. 30.
Reprinted in old style.   Biographical note of P. W. Yates.

1870.

AN Account of Anneke Janse, and Her Family ; also the Will of Anneke Janse in Dutch and English.   16°, pp. 31.
150 copies.

ANNUAL Report of the Treasurer of Union College, made May 31, 1870. Printed for the Trustees and Visitors. [Not published.] 8°, pp. 20.

BEEKMAN, JAMES W. An Address delivered before the St. Nicholas Society of the City of New York, by James W. Beekman, Saturday, Dec. 4, 1869. 8°, pp. 37.

BENEDICT, HENRY MARVIN. A Contribution to the Genealogy of the Stafford Family in America; containing an account of Col. Joab Stafford, and a complete Record of his Descendants in the Male Lines. 8°, pp. 27.
Portrait and plates. 150 copies.

BENEDICT, HENRY MARVIN. The Genealogy of the Benedicts in America. 8°, pp. xix, 475.
450 copies, and 50 large. Portraits.

BIARDO, PETRO. Missio Canadensis, Epistola et Portu-regali in Acadia transmissa ad Praepositvm Generalem Societatis Iesv, a R. Petro Biardo, ejvsdem Societatis. Secundvm exemplar emissum in Annuis Litteris Anno cIɔ, Iɔc, XI. Dilingæ Ex Typographio Mayeriana, apud Melchiorem Algeyer. Small 8°, pp. 46.
25 copies. The above imprint is calculated to mislead. The book from which the Epistle was extracted was printed by Algeyer.

BIOGRAPHICAL Notice of Peter Wraxall, Secretary of Indian Affairs for the Province of New York, and of the first Provincial Congress held in Albany, in 1754; Aid-de-Camp to Sir Wm. Johnson during the Crown Point Expedition of 1755, etc. By Daniel J. Pratt. 8°, pp. 7.

BRIEF History of the Parish of Trinity Church, Albany, N. Y., from its organization, September 4, 1829, to the consecration of the Church Edifice, Sept. 10, 1849, by the Right Rev. Bishop Whittingham. Also a continued History of the Parish to January, 1870. Compiled from the Records, by the Rev. Edward Selkirk, at the close of the twenty-sixth year of his services in the Parish as Rector. 8°, pp. 60.

BY-LAWS of Capital City Chapter No. 242, Royal Arch Masons, of the City of Albany and State of New York. Constituted February 12, A. I. 2400. 16°, pp. 78.

CATALOGUE of Books contained in the Library of the M. E. Church Sabbath School of Coxsackie. 16°, pp. 16.

CATALOGUE of Cheap and Valuable Books, comprising many scarce Books of small and elegant Editions, relating to America, Local Histories, Biographies, etc. etc. All in good order, and for Sale at the low prices affixed, by J. Munsell, dealer in new and old Books, 82 State Street, Albany, N. Y. 8°, pp. 84.

CATALOGUE of New and Second Hand Books, consisting mostly of Works on America, Local and General, Biographical and Genealogical. All in good order unless otherwise described, and offered at the low prices affixed, by J. Munsell, Albany, N. Y. 8°, pp. 54.

CATALOGUE of the Library of Park Chapel Sunday School, Albany. 16°, pp. 16.

CATALOGUE of the Officers and Alumni of the University of Alabama, 1821 to 1870. 8°, pp. 24.

CATALOGUE of the Officers and Students of the New York State Normal School, for the Fifty-first Term, ending Jan. 26, 1870. 8°, pp. 15.

CATALOGUE of the Sunday School Library of the First Lutheran Church in the City of Albany. 16°, pp. 19.

CHARLEVOIX, P. F. X. de. History and General Description of New France. Translated, with Notes, by John Gilmary Shea. Vol. IV. Sup. royal 8°, pp. 308.
    250 copies, and 50 large. Portrait, map, and plates.

CIRCULAR and Catalogue of the Law School connected with the University of Albany for the Academical Year, 1870–71. 8°, pp. 12.

CIRCULAR and Catalogue of Union College, Seventy-fourth year, 1869–70. 8°, pp. 52.

CLUTE Brothers' Steam Engine Boiler and Machine Works. 8°, pp. 36.

COLVIN, VERPLANCK. Narrative of a Bear Hunt in the Adirondacks, read before the Albany Institute, Jan. 18, 1870. 8°, pp. 16.

DeCOSTA, B. F. The Northmen in Maine; a Critical Examination of Views expressed in connection with the Subject, by Dr. J. H. [G.] Kohl in Volume I of the new series of the Maine Historical Society; to which are added Criticisms on other Portions of the Work, and a chapter on the Discovery of Massachusetts Bay. 8°, pp. 146.
    146 copies.

DISCOURSE delivered before the Pearl Street Baptist Church, August 28, 1870, on the Occasion of leaving their old House of Worship. By the Pastor, Charles DeW. Bridgman. 8°, pp. 32.

DRAKE, SAMUEL G. A Particular History of the Five Years French and Indian War in New England and Parts adjacent, from its declaration by the King of France, March 15, 1744, to the Treaty with the Eastern Indians, Oct. 16, 1749, sometimes called Governor Shirley's War; with a Memoir of Major-General Shirley, accompanied by his Portrait and other Engravings. Square 8°, pp. 312.
    Portrait and engravings.

ECHEVERRIA, GONZALES M. On Epilepsy: Anatomo-Pathological and Clinical Notes. 8°, pp. 366.
    Edition 1,000 copies, plates. Only that portion of the work from page 9 to 232 was printed by me. The author made so many changes in the work that a portion of it was reprinted, and he finally stuck fast. It was nearly two years in the press.

EIGHTH Annual Catalogue of St. Stephen's College, Annandale, N. Y., 1869–70. 8°, pp. 28.

EXERCISES Connected with the Inauguration of Rev. Charles A. Aiken, D.D., as President of Union College, Schenectady, New York, Tuesday, June 28, 1870. 8°, pp. 32.

FIFTY-NINTH Annual Report of the Albany County Bible Society. Organized A. D. 1810. 8°, pp. 18.

GARNET, ANN S. Cursory Family Sketches. 8°, pp. 140.
100 copies.

GOWANS. Catalogue of American Books, for sale at the affixed prices. Store 115 Nassau Street, New York (between Ann and Beekman Streets). 8°, pp. 32.

GRADED Question Book for Bible Classes and Sabbath Schools. In three series. First series for Small Children. By Jeremiah Wood. Vol. I. 16°, pp. 36.

GRADED Question Book for Bible Classes and Sabbath Schools. In three Series. Second Series for Youth. By Jeremiah Wood. Vol. II. 16°, pp. 41.

GRADED Question Book for Bible Classes and Sabbath Schools. In three Series. Third Series for Adults. By Jeremiah Wood. Vol. III. 16°, pp. 73.

HART, CHARLES HENRY. Bibliographia Lincolniana: an Account of the Publications occasioned by the Death of Abraham Lincoln, 16th President of the United States of America; being a Bibliographical Catalogue of all Sermons, Eulogies, Orations, etc., delivered at the time, with Notes and an Introduction. Sup. roy. 8°, pp. 86.
25 copies. A separate edition of the Introduction bound up with it, of which 100 copies were printed extra, with a special title page, rubricated.

HAVERTY, P. M. Catalogue of Books relating to Ireland and in the Irish Language, Cabinet and Stereoscopic Views of Irish Scenery and Antiquities, Irish Music, &c., &c. 8°, pp. 16.

HOMES, HENRY A. Our Knowledge of California and the North-West Coast One Hundred years since; read before the Albany Institute, February 15, 1870. 8°, pp. 20.

HOUGH, G. W. The Total Eclipse of August 7, 1869. 8°, pp. 33.
Plates.

HOWARD, NATHAN, JR. Practice Reports in the Supreme Court and the Court of Appeals of the State of New York. Vol. XXV. pp. 594.

JONES, CHARLES C., JR. Reminiscences of the Last Days, Death and Burial of Gen. Henry Lee. Square 8°, pp. 43.
125 copies.

KIDDER, FREDERIC. History of the Boston Massacre, March 5, 1770; consisting of the Narrative of the Town; the Trial of the Soldiers; and a Historical Introduction, containing unpublished Documents of John Adams, and Explanatory Notes. 8°, pp. 291.
300 copies. Plates.

LALLEMANT, CHARLES. Copie de Trois Lettres escrittes ès Années 1625, et 1626, par le P. Charles Lallemant, Superieur des Missions de la Compagnie de Iesvs en la Novvelle France. Small 8°, pp. 14.
25 copies.

LALLEMAND, CHARLES. Lettre du Reuerend Père L'Allemand, Supérieur de la Mission des Pères Iésuites, en la Nouuelle France, enuoyée de Bordeaux au R. P. Superieur du College des Iesuites à Paris, et datée du 22 Nouembre, 1629. 8°, pp. 15.
Edition 25 copies. This was printed for Dr. E. B. O'Callaghan, who had a Paris imprint put to it, agreeing with the date of Champlain's voyage, from which it was copied.

LAWS and Regulations of the Rensselaer County Mutual Benefit Association, organized 1870. 16°. pp. 6.

MEMORIAL of the Shakers against Military Duty. 8°, pp. 8.

MEMORIAL of William Lacy, Jr., who died January 31, 1870, aged 23 years. 8°, pp. 34.
Portrait.

MINUTES of the Fourth Annual Session of the Evangelical Lutheran Synod of the State of New York, held in Christ Church, Ghent, N. Y. From Thursday, Oct. 6, to Monday, Oct. 10, 1870. 8°, pp. 29.

MINUTES of the Seventy-fourth Anniversary of the Rensselaerville Association, held with the Baptist Church at New Baltimore, Greene Co., N. Y., September 7 and 8, 1870.. L. Smith, corresponding Secretary, Preston Hollow, Albany County, N. Y. 8°, pp. 6.

MUNSELL, JOEL. Collections on the History of Albany, from its Discovery to the present time, with Notices of its Public Institutions, and Biographical Sketches of Citizens deceased. Vol. III. Royal 8°, pp. viii, 498.
240 copies. Portraits and engravings.

MUNSELL, JOEL. Webster's Calendar, or the Albany Almanac for the year of our Lord 1869. 12°, pp. 36.

NASON, ELIAS. A Memoir of Mrs. Susanna Rowson, with Elegant and Illustrative Extracts from her Writings in Prose and Poetry, 8°, pp. 212.
200 copies. Portrait engraved at the expense of one of her pupils, at a cost $150.

NORTON, JOHN. Narrative of the Capture and Burning of Fort Massachusetts by the French and Indians, in the Time of the War of 1744–1749, and the Captivity of all those Stationed there, to the Number of thirty persons; written at the Time by one of the Captives, the Rev. Mr. John Norton, Chaplain of the Fort. Now first published, with Notes, by Samuel G. Drake. Square 8°, pp. 51.
100 copies.

NEILL, EDWARD D. History of the Virginia Company of London, with Letters to and from the First Colony, never before printed. Square 8°, pp. xvi, 432.
200 copies. Portrait.

PECK, CHARLES F.　Fungi.　8°, pp. 13.

PLEA for an Endowment for St. Stephen's College.　A Sermon preached in various Churches of the Dioceses of New York, Long Island, and Albany.　By Robert B. Fairbairn, D.D., Warden of St. Stephen's College, Annandale, N. Y.　8°, pp. 23.

PRATT, DANIEL J.　Manual of the Albany Institute: prepared under the order of the Institute, March, 1870.　8°, pp. 47.
　250 copies.

PROCEEDINGS of the Fifty-seventh Anniversary of the Washington County Bible Society, and other Anniversaries of Benevolent Associations, held at East Greenwich, N. Y., Sept. 1st and 2d, 1869.　12°, pp. 35.

SECULAR View of Religion in the State, and the Bible in the Public Schools.　By E. P. Hurlbut.　8°, pp. 55.

SEPTUAGENARIAN Dinner.　Report of the Speeches, Poem and other Proceedings at a Dinner given June 30, 1870, by the citizens of Pittsfield, Mass., to their Townsmen who had reached the age of 70 years.　Official Report.　8°, pp. 48.

SMITH, E. PESHINE.　Reports of Cases argued and determined in the Court of Appeals of the State of New York.　8°, pp. 602.

SMITH, WILLIAM R.　Reports of Decisions in the Supreme Court of the State of Alabama, originally prepared by Henry Minor, George N. Stewart, Stewart and Porter, and Benjamin F. Porter: a new edition with Notes and Digest.　5 vols., 8°.

STILES, HENRY R.　A History of the City of Brooklyn, including the old Town and Village of Brooklyn, the Town of Bushwick, and the Village and City of Williamsburgh.　Vol. III.　Royal 8°, pp. viii, 480.
　1180 copies of three sizes.　Portraits and plates.

THE Young People's Society of the State street Presbyterian Church, Rev. G. C. Heckman, Pastor, Albany, N. Y.　16°, pp. 20.

THIRTY-FOURTH Annual Report of the Albany City Tract and Missionary Society, presented at the Annual Meeting, in the Congregational Church, December 19, 1869.　8°, pp. 24.
　1,000 copies.

TRANSACTIONS of the Albany Institute.　Vol. VI.　8°, pp. iv, 382.
　Plates.

TWENTY-Second Annual Report of the Inspectors and Superintendent of the Albany Penitentiary, with the Accompanying Documents.　Made December 13, 1870.　8°, pp. 76.

UNIVERSITY of Albany.　8°, pp. 8.

UNIVERSITY of Albany.　Department of Medicine.　Circular and Catalogue. Albany Medical College.　Thirty-ninth Session, 1869–70.　8°, pp. 16.

1871.

ATLANTIC Mutual Life Insurance Company. Home Office: Albany, N. Y. 16°, pp. 36.

CATALOGUE of Books in the Library of the First Congregational Sabbath School. 16°, pp. 32.

CATALOGUE of the Library of the Congregational Church Sabbath School, Gloversville, N. Y. 16°, pp. 22.

CATALOGUE of the Library of the Watervliet Union Sunday School. 16°. pp. 8.

CATALOGUE of the Officers and Students of the Law School connected with the University of Albany for the Academical Year 1870–71. 8°, pp. 16.

CATALOGUE of the Officers and Students of the New York State Normal School, for the Fifty-third Term, ending Jan. 25, 1871. 8°, pp. 16.

DESCRIPTIVE Catalogue of Vegetable Seeds, raised at New Lebanon, N. Y. With directions for their Cultivation. All orders should be directed to D. C. Brainard, Mount Lebanon. N. Y. 8°, pp. 23.
Woodcuts.

LAWS of Union College, as Revised and Enacted January 24, 1871. 8°, pp. 24.

NEWBURY, A. & B., Manufacturers of Country Newspaper Presses, Proof Presses, Paper Cutters, Job and Card Presses, Iron Imposing Beds, Composing Sticks, Mitering Machines, Lead Cutters, &c. Also Iron and Brass Castings, Grist and Saw Mill Irons, Steam Engines, and Machinery of every description to order. Coxsackie, Greene County, N. Y. 8°. pp. 16.
Woodcuts of Machinery.

REGLEMENTEN en Regels van Orde voor de Nederlandsche Vereeniging tot Ondersteuning van Behoeftige Landgenooten, opgerigt den 23 November, 1869, te Albany, N. Y. Onder den zinspreuk: Hoe schoon is het Broeders vereenigd te zien. 16°, pp. 16.

Titles Omitted in Proper Places.

1857.

Address delivered before the New York State Agricultural Society at the Annual Meeting in Albany, February 11, 1857, by Theodore S. Faxton, President, and the address of Alonzo S. Upham, on taking the Chair as President elect. Published by order of the Society. 8°, pp. 23.

1859.

Review of the Decision of the Court of Appeals upon the Manor Question. 8°, pp. 87.

1860.

Catalogue of the Law School of the University of Albany, for the Fall Term of 1860. 8°, pp. 16.

Collections of the Ulster Historical Society. Volume I, part 2. 8°, pp. 177.

Tenth Annual Report of the Troy Conference Missionary Society, Auxiliary to the Missionary Society of the Methodist Episcopal Church, for the Year ending April 11, 1860. 8°, pp. 56.

1861.

Catalogue and Circular of the Albany Medical College. Circular for 1861. 8°, pp. 8.

Righteous entering into Peace. A Sermon on the death of Abraham F. Lansing, preached in the Second Reformed Protestant Dutch Church in the City of Albany, 21st April, 1861. By the Pastor, Rev. Isaac N. Wyckoff, D.D. 8°, pp. 28.

Troy Conference Meth. Episcopal Church Directory, Session at the Hudson Street M. E. Church, Albany, April 17, 1861. Together with the Anniversary Exercises. 8°, pp. 8.

1862.

Annual Reports of the Officers and Standing Committees of the Albany Methodist S. S. Union, made at its Eighth Annual Meeting, Jan. 20, 1862. Published by order of the Union. 8°, pp. 18.

BRIEF Sketches of the Officers who were in the Battle of Lake Erie. By Usher Parsons, M. D.   8°, pp. 13.

CARRIER's Address to the Patrons of the Albany Morning Express, January 1, 1862.   8°, pp. 4.

CATALOGUE of the Law School of the University of Albany for the Fall Term of 1862.   Published by the Class.   8°, pp. 7.

ORDER of Exercises at the Dedication of the State Street Presbyterian Church, October 12, 1862, Albany, N. Y.   8°, pp. 4.

POEM delivered before the Montgomery County Agricultural Society at Fonda, October 9, 1861, by John Bowdish, Esq.   8°, pp. 24.

1863.

ADDRESS delivered at the Centennial Celebration of the Incorporation of New Boston, New Hampshire, July 4, 1863, by Clark B. Cochrane. 8°, pp. 44.

ADDRESS delivered in the Evangelical Lutheran Ebenezer Church, Albany, on occasion of the Funeral of Mrs. Susan C. Pohlman, wife of the Rev. Henry N. Pohlman, D.D., Nov. 10, 1862, by William B. Sprague, D.D. Printed by request of the Church Council.   8°, pp 18.

CIRCULAR and Catalogue of the Law School of the University of Albany, for the years 1862–3.   8°, pp. 16.

COMPLETED Christian Life.   A Sermon commemorative of Adjt. Richard M. Strong, 177th Regt. N. Y. S. V., who died at Bonnet Carré, La., May 12, 1863.   Preached in the State street Presbyterian Church, Albany, N. Y., by Rev. A. S. Twombly, June 7, 1863.   8°, pp. 22.

GREAT Rebellion.   An Address delivered in the M. E. Church, Nassau, N. Y., August 6th, 1863, by Rev. F. A. Soule.   Published by request. 8°, pp. 20.

MUNSELL's Guide to the Hudson River by Railroad and Steamboat. With a Colored Map, representing every Town, Village, Landing, Railroad Station, and Point of Interest on or adjacent to the Hudson River, from Staten Island to Troy, with minute Descriptions and References, for the convenience of the Business Man and the Traveler.   16°, pp. 56.

ORIGINAL Planning and Construction of Bunker Hill Monument.   By S. Swett.   With Engravings.   8°, pp. 11.

RISE and Progress of Methodism in Cobleskill Centre, Schoharie County, N. Y.   By David Shank.   8vo, pp. 8.

SECOND Annual Catalogue of St. Stephen's College, Annandale, 1863–4. 8°, pp. 16.

SERMON preached in the Chapel of St. Stephen's College, Annandale, on All Saint's Day, 1863.   By Robert B. Fairbairn, M.A.   8°, pp. 19.

SERMON preached on the Fourth Sabbath of Oct. 25th, 1863, occasioned by the Death of William Crounse, who died at Port Hudson, in the service of his Country. By Rev. William P. Davis, A.M. 8°, pp. 23.

SKETCH of the Life of Rev. Michael Wigglesworth, A.M., author of the Day of Doom. By John Ward Dean. To which is appended a fragment of his Autobiography, some of his Letters, and a Catalogue of his Library. 8°, pp. 20.

1864.

ACCOUNT of the Discovery of an Ancient Ship on the Eastern Shore of Cape Cod. By Amos Otis. 8°, pp. 10.

ADDRESS at the Funeral of Mrs. Melenda B. Cushman, on the 27th July, A.D. 1863. By Rev. Samuel G. Willard. 8°, pp. 16.

AFFAIRS at Fort Chartres, 1768–1781. 4°, pp. 12.

DISCOURSE occasioned by the Death of Mr. Samuel Patten, preached in the Washington Avenue Baptist Church, at Albany, N. Y., July 24, 1864. By Rev. W. P. Everett. 8°, pp. 32.

DISCOURSE on the Death of Rev. John Spoor, preached at Freehold, on Saturday, April 2, 1864. By Warren Hathaway. Published by request. 8°, pp. 32.

HISTORICAL Sketch of the Old Church, Quincy, Mass. By Rev. Frederic A. Whitney. 8°, pp. 17.

MEMORANDA of the Preston Family. By Orlando Brown. 4° pp. 26.

1865.

ASSASSINATION of Abraham Lincoln : a Discourse delivered in the State St. Pres. Church by Rev. A. S. Twombly, Sunday morning, April 16, 1865. 8°, pp. 18.

CHURCH and the Times: Annual Address delivered before the New York Eastern Christian Conference, on Thursday, June 1, 1865, at its Forty-Seventh Session, held at Freehold, Greene Co. N. Y., by Rev. Warren Hathaway. 8° pp. 23.

DISCOURSE occasioned by the Death of Abraham Lincoln: preached at Coxsackie, on Wednesday, April 19, 1865, by Warren Hathaway. 8°, pp. 24.

DISCOURSE on the Death of Mrs. Mary Earle, wife of George Earle, Esq., and only surviving Daughter of Jeremiah Carpenter, Esq., delivered at Valatie, Columbia County, N. Y., Tuesday, May 9, 1865. By Rev. William Whittaker. 8°, pp. 13.

FOURTH Annual Catalogue of St. Stephen's College, Annandale, N. Y., 1865-6. 8°, pp. 22.

MEMORIAL of the Rev. D. F. Heller, late Pastor of the Lutheran Church of St. Paul's, West Camp, N. Y. By the Rev. Thomas Lape. 8°, pp. 8.

OUR National Sorrow. A Discourse on the Death of Abraham Lincoln, containing the substance of two Sermons delivered in the Presbyterian Church, Johnstown, April 16 and 19, 1865. By Rev. Daniel Stewart, D.D. 8°, pp. 20.

TRUTH and Righteousness Triumphant. A Discourse commemorative of the Death of President Lincoln : preached in the Washington Avenue M. E. Church, April 20, 1865. By B. Hawley, D.D. 8°, pp. 20.

1866.

ANNUAL Reports of the Officers and Standing Committees of the Albany Methodist S. S. Union, made at its Twelfth Annual Meeting, January 15, 1866. Published by order of the Union. 8°, pp. 25.

CIRCULAR and Catalogue of the Law School of the University of Albany, for the Year 1865-6. 8°, pp. 16.

UNIVERSITY of Albany. Albany Medical College, Circular and Catalogue Thirty-sixth Session. 1866-7. 8°, pp. 16.

WORDS spoken in the Second Presbyterian Church, Albany May 2, 1864, at the Obsequies of the Late Colonel Lewis Benedict. By the Rev. C. DeW. Bridgman. 8°, pp. 12.

1867.

ADDRESS at the Funeral of Mrs. John Steward, at Grace Church, N. Y., 1st of August, 1867. By Rev. Stephen H. Tyng, D.D. 8°, pp. 8.

ANNUAL Report of the Treasurer of Union College, made June 29, 1867. Printed for the Trustees and Visitors. 8°, pp. 18.

CIRCULAR and Catalogue of the Law School of the University of Albany, for the Year 1866-7. 8°, pp. 16.

CATALOGUE of the Law School of the University of Albany, for the Fall Term of 1867. Published by the Class. 8°, pp. 10.

FIFTH Annual Catalogue of St. Stephen's College, Annandale, N. Y., 1866-7. 8°, pp. 30.

FIFTIETH Annual Report of the Bible Society of Fulton and Hamilton Counties, presented at Gloversville, September 3, 1867. With Statistics. 8°, pp. 29.

FIRST Bulletin of the Class of 1866, Union College. November, 1867. 8°, pp. 11.

NINETEENTH Annual Report of the Inspectors of the Albany Penitentiary, with the accompanying documents. Made 12th December, 1867. 8°, pp. 35.

SERMON preached at the Funeral of Dr. A. W. Hull, April 15, 1867, by Rev. Wm. J. Blain, and Remarks by M. S. Goodale, D.D. Printed at the request of the Family. 8°, pp. 16.

SIXTH Annual Catalogue of St. Stephen's College, Annandale, N. Y. 1867–68. 8°, pp. 28.

THIRD Bulletin of the Class of 1864, Union College. November 1, 1867. 8°, pp. 28.

UNIVERSITY of Albany. Department of Medicine. Albany Medical College Circular and Catalogue. Thirty-Seventh Session. 1867–8. 8°, pp. 10.

UNIVERSITY of Albany. Historical Sketches of the Medical College, the, Law School, and the Dudley Observatory. From the Historical Collections of Albany, 1867. 8°, pp. 31.

1868.

ADDRESS delivered on occasion of the Funeral of the Rev. William James, D.D., in the First Presbyterian Church, Albany, Wednesday, February 19, 1868. By William B. Sprague, D.D. Printed by request of the bereaved family. 8°, pp. 22.

ANNUAL Report of the Treasurer of Union College, made May 30, 1868. Printed for the Trustees and Visitors. 8°, pp. 19.

ARTICLES of Faith and Covenant, together with the Principles of Government and Discipline, adopted by the First Congregational Church, Albany. Published for the use of the Members. 8°, pp. 28.

CATALOGUE of the Officers and Students and Register of Societies in Union College. 1868–9. Issued by the Senior Class. 8°. pp. 72.
Engraving.

CATALOGUE of the Officers and Students of the Law School connected with the University of Albany for the Academical Year 1868–69. 8°, pp. 16.

CIRCULAR and Catalogue of Union College, Seventy-Third year, First Term, 1868. 8°, pp. 42.

CONSTITUTION and Rules of Order of the Evangelical Lutheran Synod of the State of New York. 8°, pp. 14.

HISTORY of the Albany City Hospital, and Extracts from Addresses delivered in its behalf, by James H. Armsby, M.D., in 1851–1852. 8°, pp. 48.

IMPRESSIONS of Prison Life in Great Britain. Submitted to the Inspectors and Superintendent of the Albany Penitentiary. By David Dyer. Published by their Request. 8°, pp. 25.

MEMORIAM. Stephen Van Rensselaer. Born 1789. Died 1868. 8°, pp. 34.

MINUTES of the Second Annual Session of the Evangelical Lutheran Synod of the State of New York, held in St. Paul's Church, Wurtemberg, from Thursday, October 15th, to Tuesday, October 20th, 1868. 8°, pp. 35.

MISCELLANEOUS List of Valuable and Interesting Books, on sale for cash at the prices affixed, by J. Munsell, 82 State street. Albany, N. Y. 8°, pp. 32.

RULES, Regulations and By-Laws, for the Government and Discipline of the Albany County Penitentiary. 8°, pp. 36.

STRONG & DOUW's Agricultural Almanac, 1868, at Albany, N. Y. Large 8°, pp. 30.
    Illustrated with cuts of agricultural implements.

TWENTIETH Annual Report of the Inspectors of the Albany Pententiary, with the accompanying Documents. Made 16th December, 1868. With appendix: Impressions of Prison Life in Great Britain. 8°, pp. 65.

UNIVERSITY of Albany. Historical Sketches of the Medical College, the Law School, and the Dudley Observatory. From the Historical Collections of Albany, vol. I. 8°, pp. 16.

WITHOUT DATE.

BIBLIOTHECA Americana. Catalogue of a Large and Valuable Collection of Books relating to America, and Voyages and Travels for sale at the prices annexed, by J. W. Bouton, 481 Broadway, New York. 4°, pp. 24.

BIBLIOTHECA Americana. Catalogue of an Extensive and Valuable Collection of Books relating to America, comprising Revolutionary, Local and State Histories, Antiquities, Rare Historical Tracts, Early Voyages and Travels, Works on the Indians, and the War of 1812–15, American Biography, Magazines, Genealogies, Statistics, Gazetteers, and Geographies, etc. etc. etc. Many of which are enriched by the insertion of Autograph Letters, Extra Portraits, Newspaper Clippings, etc., from the Library of the Celebrated Antiquary, Collector, and Author. Samuel G. Drake, Esq., of Boston, for sale at the prices annexed, by J. W. Bouton & Co., 87 Walker Street, New York. 4°, pp. 36.

BROADWAY M. E. Sunday School. 8°, pp. 8.

CATALOGUE of a Large and Valuable Collection of Rare, Standard and Miscellaneous English Books, lately received from London, and for sale at the reasonable Prices affixed, by J. W. Bouton, 481 Broadway (near Broome Street), New York (Late J. W. Bouton & Co., of 87 Walker St.). 4°, pp. 24.

MEMOIR of Lewis C. Beck. 4°, pp. 12.

MEMOIR of Theodric Romeyn Beck. 4°, pp. 15.

ORGANIZATION of the Militia. 4°, pp. 12.

INDEX.

Goody Two Shoes, 35.
Gospel Crown of Life. 47.
Gospel, the, in its First Progress Westward, 56.
Gould, George. 111.
Gould, James, 111.
Gould, William, 118.
Gowans, William, 77, 85, 92, 99, 106, 111, 117, 123, 130, 136, 142, 144, 149, 154, 158, 163.
Grace Church, Sermon, 51 ; Address, 170.
Grace, Discourses on, 24
Graded Question Book, 163.
Grammar, Principles of, 30.
Grand Encampment, I. O. of O. F., By-laws, 110.
Grand Officers, Reports of, 108.
Grant, Matthew, his old Church Record, 99.
Graves, William J., 9.
Gravier, Jacques, 85, 114.
Great Barrington Academy Catalogue, 51.
Great Western Turnpike Road, charter, 44.
Great Western Rail Road Company, C. W., Articles of Agreement, 51.
Greenbush, Charter, 51, 82.
Greenbush Methodist Sunday School Library, Catalogue, 142.
Green Island Directory, 114.
Greenville Lodge, No. 394, I. O. of O. F., By-laws, 40.
Greenwich Congregational Church Manual, 99.
Greenwood, R. J., 64, 77.
Groesbeck, Brigadier General John, 15.
Groesbeeck, Stephen, 40.
Griffin, P. H., 84.
Grimes, J. Stanley, 12.
Guignas, 114.
Guild, Reuben A., 92.
Guilderland Mutual Insurance Association, By-laws, 61.
Gunn, Rev. Walter, 52.

Hackett, W. V., 117.
Haldeman S. S., 29.
Hale, Benjamin, 6.
Hall, Benjamin H., 136.
Hall, Fitz Edward, Catalogue of Books, 149, 148.
Hall, Hiland, 154.
Hall, Professor James, 77, 123, 154.
Hall, Joseph, 144.
Hall W. C., 77.
Halleck, Fitz Greene, 105.
Halley, Ebenezer, 29, 40.
Halliwell, James Orchard, 123.
Hamilton College, Examination, 158.
Hamilton County Teachers' Institute, 139.
Hamilton, James A., 78.
Hamilton, Oration, Commemorative of the Character of, 49.
Hammond, Jabez D., 46.
Hammond, S. S., 46.
Hammond, Wells S., 10.
Hamor, Ralph, 106.
Hand, Samuel, 110.
Hardware, Sale Catalogue, 26.
Harmonia, the, 62.
Harris, Edward Doubleday, 117.
Harris, Judge, 53, 134.
Harris, Thomas L., 26.
Harris's Therapeutics, 26.
Harrison, William Henry, 14.
Harsha, David A., 46, 52, 64, 130, 136, 144.
Harsha, John W., 58

Hart, Charles Henry, 163.
Hartwick Theological and Classical Seminary, Annual Catalogue, 35, 39, 44, -49, 56, 61, 68, 75, 82, 89, 90, 97, 103, 110, 114, 120, 127, 141, 157 ; Memorial Volume, 151 ; Addresses, 40.
Hartwick Synod Evangelical Lutheran Church, Minutes, 6, 10, 42, 47, 51, 59, 65, 72, 79, 86, 91, 107, 112, 124, 131, 145, 151.
Hastings, Hugh J., 13.
Hatfield and Deerfield,Papers on the Attack on, 99.
Hathaway, Rev. Warren, 136, 169,
Haven, C. W., 46.
Haverty, P. M., 150, 158, 163.
Hawley, B., D.D., 170.
Hawley, Gideon, Referee, 11, 52, 70, 78.
Hawley's Sermon, 136.
Hayden Family, Genealogy, 58.
Haynes, 117.
Healing of the Nations, 71.
Health, Preservation of, 24.
Heart Lyrics, 156.
Heaton, Mr., 135.
Heckman, Rev. G. C., 165.
Heermance, John C., 32.
Helderbergia, 73.
Helderberg War, 13.
Heller, Rev. D. F., 137, 169.
Hemenway, Abby Maria, 117, 123.
Henderson, Kennedy & Kneeland, Catalogue, 76.
Henry, Patrick, Oration on, 41, 55.
Hepinstall, Geo., Assignees' Sale, 75.
Hercules, a Poem, 81.
Herkimer County, History of, 75.
Herr, Rudolph, 70.
Hertzell, Mrs., 43.
Hervey, Rev. James, 136.
Hessian Fly, 26.
Hewes, S. E., 90, 96.
Heyes, Henry, 36.
Hickcox, Hamlet H., 124.
Hickcox, John H., 92, 144.
Hill, Nicholas, Jr., 44.
Hillsdale Mercantile Association, Constitution, 70.
Hill, William, 78.
Historical Magazine, 132.
History of Civilization, 154, 158.
History of Vermont, 154.
Hitchcock, O. B., 117.
Hochstrasser, Jacob, Administrator's Sale, 30.
Hodgman, Jennette, 137.
Hoffman & Munsell, 47.
Hoffman & White, 13.
Holcroft, Thomas, 58.
Holden, A. W., 46.
Holgate, Jerome B., 32, 58.
Holmes, Edwin, 6, 8, 12, 14, 16, 17, 21, 23, 26, 29, 32, 36, 40, 46.
Holt Family, Genealogy, 129.
Holt, William, 129.
Holy Innocents, Church of the, Sermon, 100, 113.
Holy Scriptures, Bibliography of, 113.
Home of the Friendless, Annual Report, 61, 75.
Home, Sweet Home, 71, 77.
Homes, Henry A., 123, 136, 163.
Homœopathy Contrasted with Allopathy, Lecture, 93.
Homœopathy Illustrated, 17.
Homœopathic Medical Society of the State of New York, Proceedings, 47, 58, 60, 61, 66.

Torrey, Mary Anne, 25.
Torreys, Professor, 73.
Tory's Guard, Doom of the, 20.
Total Eclipse, 163.
Townsend, Franklin, 60, 74.
Townsend, Franklin & Co., 35.
Townsend's Furnace Pattern List, 87.
Townsend, Howard, 60, 126, 132, 147, 150.
Townsend, John F., 67.
Townsend's Pattern List, 139.
Townsend, Theodore, 60.
Towners Family Genealogy, 117.
Tracts for the People, Baptist, 18.
Trade and Commerce of the City of Albany, 132.
Trade Directory of Albany, 59.
Tranchepain, St. Augustine de, 102.
Transactions Albany Institute, 53.
Trappers of New York, 43, 109.
Trask, William B., 126.
Trees, Fruit and Ornamental, Catalogue, 54.
Tremont Temple, Boston, 87.
Trenck, Baron Frederick, Life of, 58
Trial, the, 45.
Trichina Spiralis, 159.
Trinity Church, Albany, 48; Tract, 91; History of, 161.
Trinity Church, New York, Sermon, 56, 94; Title, 74, 81; Bill, Debates, 84; Bill, Speech on the, 88.
Trot, Dame, 33.
Troy Almanac, 117, 119, 120.
Troy Conference of the M. E. Church, Minutes, 24, 29.
Troy Conference Academy, 25th Annual Announcement, 109; Catalogue, 63.
Troy Conference Miscellany, 66.
Troy Conference Missionary Society Report, 20, 54, 88, 167.
Troy Directory, 82, 97, 103, 114, 126, 133.
Troy, Mysteries of, 28,
Troy, Reminiscences of, 108.
Troy Young Men's Association, Catalogue Library, 98.
Troyes, A., 105.
Truth, etc., Triumphant, 170.
Tuthill, Franklin, 102.
Tweddle Hall, Poem on Opening, 107.
Twin Brothers, 20, 23, 28.
Twombly, Rev. A. S., 133, 141, 151, 168, 169.
Tyler, R. H., 148.
Tyndale Family Genealogy, 117.
Tyng, Rev. Stephen H., 170.
Typographical Miscellany, 41.

Uebelacker, A., 86.
Ulster and Delaware Co. Farmers' Almanac, 120.
Ulster Historical Society, paper, 113; Collections of, 167, 113.
Unadilla Academy, Catalogue, 57.
Unadilla, new County, 38.
Union College, 30, 120; Address, 29; Annual Report, 161, 170, 171; Bulletin of the Class of, 62, 170, 171; Burial of Mechanics, 122,128; Catalogue, 104, 120, 121,126, 128, 134, 155, 162, 171; Catalogue Library, 121; Chemical Society Bulletin, 125; Chemical Society of, By-laws, 122; Inauguration Exercises, 163; Investigation into the Affairs of, 66; Laws, 166; Magazine, 120, 126; Memorial, 133; Oration, 28; Songs, 122; Treasurer's Report, 119, 125, 127, 133, 141 : Union Resumé, 120.
Unionist, the, 13.
Union Nurseries, Catalogue, 54.
Union Resolutions, Speech, 48.

Union Village Academy, Catalogue, 8; Congregation Church, Manual, 106.
Unitarian Church, Discourse, 127.
Unitarian Sunday School Library, Catalogue, 143.
Unitarian Society, Sermon, 147.
United States Hotel, Entertainment, 18.
Universalism, 19.
Universalist Church, Albany, Discourse, 19.
Universities. English, 66.
University of Albany Associated Congress of the Law Department, Constitution of, 116.
University of Albany, 165; Historical Sketches, 171, 141.
University of the State of New York, Visitation, 120.
Upham, Alonzo S., 166, 167.
Upham, Ebenezer P., 12.
Usury Laws, 6.

Valatie Fire Engine Co. No. 4, Constitution, 19; First Presbyterian Church, Confession of Faith, 62.
Valentine, T. W., 55, 67.
Van Antwerp, 48.
Van Brunt Family, Genealogy of the, 148.
Van Buren, John, 44.
Van Buren, Martin, 40.
Vanderburgh, F., 49.
Vanderpool, James, 16.
Van Dyck, Missionary, 72.
Van Dyk, Henry H., 38.
Van Horne, David, 126.
Van Loan's Farmers' Almanac, 120.
Van Olinda, Capt. Abram, 34.
Van Rensselaer Family Grants, 21.
Van Rensselaer Manor, Synopsis, 42.
Van Rensselaer, William P., 53.
Van Santvoord, George, 123.
Van Schaack, Eliza T., 192.
Van Schaack, Henry C., 102.
Van Schaick, Egbert, 19.
Van Schaick, John B., 7.
Van Vechten, Hon. Teunis, 101.
Van Voorst, Hooper C., 28.
Van Wormer and McGarvey's Price List, 81, 142.
Vassal Genealogy, 126.
Vegetable Seed Catalogue, 166.
Vegetation, the true Philosophy of, 83.
Verhandlungen, 96.
Vermilye, Thomas E., 7, 9, 11.
Vermont, Eastern, History of, 136.
Vermont Gazetteer, 117.
Vesta Division Sons of Temperance, By-laws, 31.
Vickers Family Genealogy, 117, 133.
Vincent, Marvin R., 153.
Violin Preceptor, 42, 66.
Virginia Company of London, History, of, 164.
Voice of God, 29.
Vose & Co., 40, 59.
Votes and Proceedings of the Assembly of the State of New York, Fourth session, 102.
Voyage of George Clark, 151.
Voyage to New York, 149.
Voyages of Discovery, Early, 46.
Voyages of St. John and Arms, 151.

Wadsworth, Mr., 88.
Wadsworth Lodge No. 417, F. & A. M., By-laws, 97.
Wait, Thomas G., 5.
Walker, Aaron G., 49.
Walker's Dictionary, 34, 43.